RAYMOND

Wicked Wretched Wraith Men :

Earl Harold Paul Immortal Man

HARRISON

MOUNT HARRISON PICTURES STUDIOS
P R E S S

EL Segundo California

Wicked Wretched Wraith Men
/Earl Harold Paul Immortal Man Book Seven
Copyright © 2006 by Raymond Harrison
Published by Mount Harrison Pictures Studios Press Copyright © March 2006
Enjoy your Official Raymond Harrison website! Visit www.enjoyraymondharrison.com today!

Printed in the United States of America

First Edition
ISBN: 13 978-09779067-0-3
ISBN: 10 0-9779067-0-1

Library of Congress Number: 200692231

The Writers Guild of America, west, Inc.
Registration numbers: 1095172(1st draft); 1129915(5th draft);

Mount Harrison Pictures Studios Press
214 Main Street Suite 341
El Segundo, CA 90245

Book Cover & Interior Page Design: Raymond Harrison
Photography: Fotogenix Portraits "Memories Captured Daily" Orem Utah
Visit www.fotogenix.net today!

"Mount Harrison Pictures Studios Suite", "Lord of Hope Hymn Suite",
"Death Song Suite" and "Wicked Wretched Wraith Men Suite"
"The Story Worlds of Fiction Suite"
music and lyrics by Raymond Harrison

To order more copies of Wicked Wretched Wraith Men
/Earl Harold Paul Immortal Man A Screenplay Book Seven

Phone 1-800 booklog
FAX: 491-589-4040

Or write to:
BookMasters Distribution/Fulfillment
30 Amberwood Parkway
Ashland, OH 44805

Manufactured by BookMasters Inc. Mansfield, Ohio 44905
Visit www.bookmasters.com and www.atlasbooks.com today!

Or visit online today:

www.enjoyraymondharrison.com

To write to Mr. Harrison himself, address you letters to:
Raymond Harrison Fan Club
214 Main Street Suite 341
El Segundo, CA 90245

"Enjoy your new birthplace of imagination..."
Mount Harrison Pictures Studios
Visit www.mountharrisonpicturesstudios.com today!

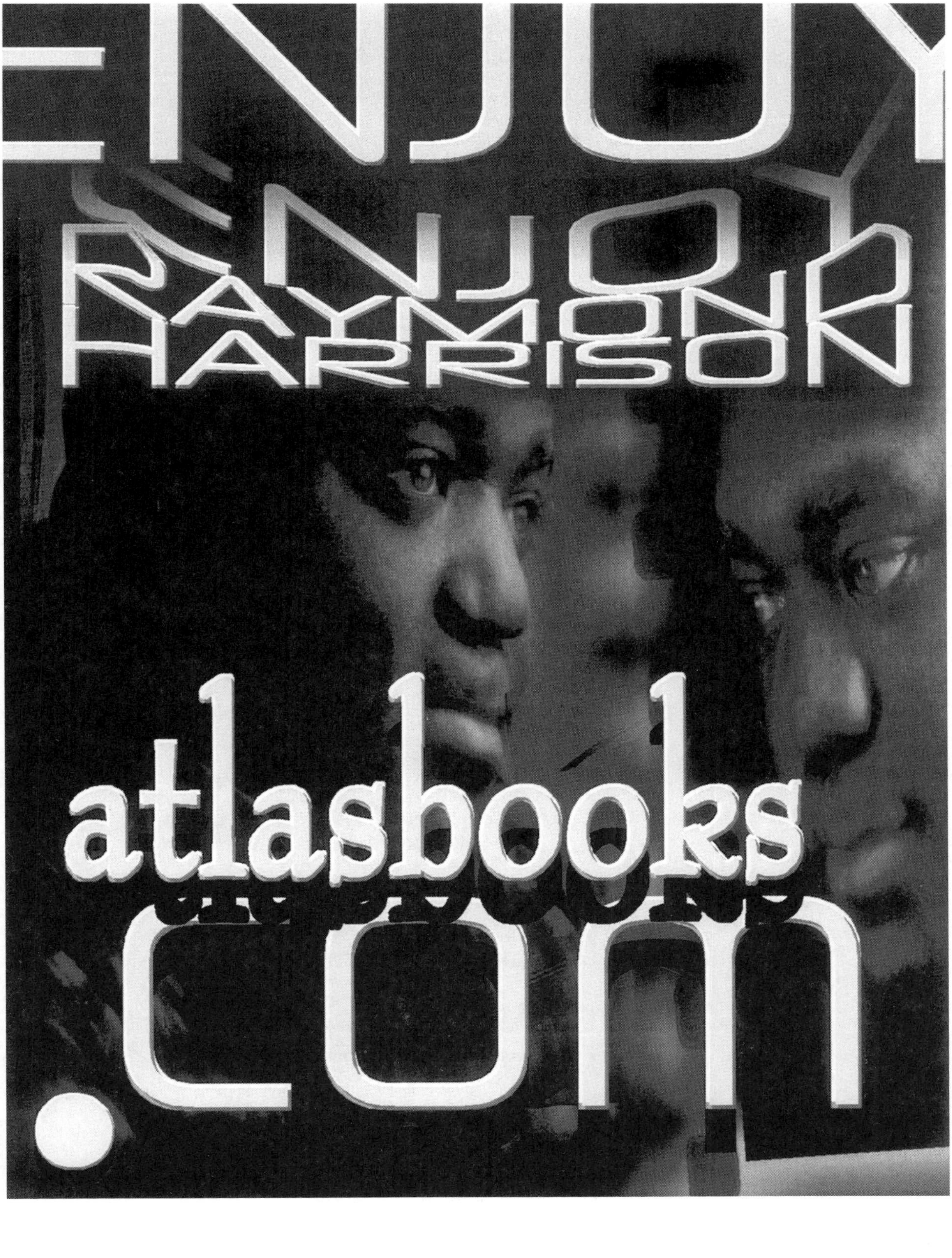
ENJOY
RAYMOND
HARRISON
atlasbooks
.com

Stay tooned...
Enjoy your upcoming
Paperback Screenplays and Hardcover Novels
The Imagination Library Works of Raymond Harrison
Coming Soon from
Mount Harrison Pictures Studios Press

Hardcover Novels

Antarctica 5888 A.D.
Wicked Wretched Wraith Men /Book Seven: Earl Harold Paul Immortal Man
Wicked Wretched Wraith Men /Book Eight: Blood Bath Las Vegas Style!
Wicked Wretched Wraith Men /Book Nine: Return to Maple Mary

Panther X in...
Monrovia Spaceport Metropolis Liberia 7076 A.D. COVERT CHAPTER 1
Monrovia Spaceport Metropolis Liberia 7076 A.D. COVERT CHAPTER 2
Monrovia Spaceport Metropolis Liberia 7076 A.D. COVERT CHAPTER 3

Mathua Havilah in... Ethiopia 3378 B.C.

The Adventures of Androibot Man

Philadelphia Palace Grand Casino Resort /Las Vegas Nevada USA

Paperback Screenplays

Antarctica 5888 A.D.
Wicked Wretched Wraith Men /Book Eight: Blood Bath Las Vegas Style!
Wicked Wretched Wraith Men /Book Nine: Return to Maple Mary

Panther X in...
Monrovia Spaceport Metropolis Liberia 7076 A.D. COVERT CHAPTER 1
Monrovia Spaceport Metropolis Liberia 7076 A.D. COVERT CHAPTER 2
Monrovia Spaceport Metropolis Liberia 7076 A.D. COVERT CHAPTER 3

Mathua Havilah in...Ethiopia 3378 B.C.

The Adventures of Androibot Man

Philadelphia Palace Grand Casino Resort /Las Vegas Nevada USA

RAYMOND HARRISON

Blood Bath Las Vegas Style

Wicked Wretched Wraith Men

A SCREENPLAY

Book Eight

RAYMOND HARRISON

Return To Maple Mary

Wicked Wretched

Wraith Men

A SCREENPLAY

Book Nine

RAYMOND HARRISON

A SCREENPLAY

ANTARCTICA

5 8 8 8

A. D.

RAYMOND HARRISON

Panther X

A SCREENPLAY

film ...

Covert Chapter

0LEG

MONROVIA

SPACEPORT METROPOLIS LIBERIA

2016 A.D.

RAYMOND HARRISON

Panther X

A SCREENPLAY

film ....

Covert Chapter TWO

MONROVIA

SPACEPORT METROPOLIS LIBERIA

2016 A.D.

RAYMOND HARRISON

Panther X

A SCREENPLAY

film

Covert Chapter Three

MONROVIA

SPACEPORT
METROPOLIS
LIBERIA
2015 AD

The 1930 Baton Rouge Tale of the Vampire Composer
Count Gamba Babatunji

RAYMOND HARRISON

US. MARSHAL
Eleanora Martha
Robinson

Episodes

A Screenplay

RAYMOND HARRISON

The Adventures of

ANDROIBOT MAN

A SCREENPLAY

RAYMOND HARRISON a screenplay

Philadephia Palace Grand

Las Vegas Nevada USA

Casino Resort

Mathua

Havilah

in ...

Ethiopia 3380 B.C.

Raymond Harrison

A SCREENPLAY
Book One

Harrison's Imaginary Library Works presents A Synopsis Collection
written by Raymond Harrison

**Upcoming Paperback Screenplays and Hard Cover Novels
Coming Soon for Your Enjoyment !**

**The O.G.O.F.R. FORCE Orders : Benjamin William Snow,
code name Panther X is hereby ordered to travel to the city of...**

As in all of his adventurous and dangerous covert operations...**Panther X** must apprehend a **Bishop** of the order of the **Sons of the Greater One** for his religious **crimes** against humanity. Each **mission** operation is simply called **Old Glory Operation Freedom Reigns**, until the world is complete rid of the Sons of the Greater One terrorists **cells**. These cells have **Supreme Overseers** who belong to a secret society of **fanatical clergymen** and **women**; This **religious** sect believes in giving their Deity **glory** with their acts of violence they inflict upon themselves and others. Located all over the world in **cloud cities**, underground **caverns**, at the bottom of the **ocean floor** and in all seven continents are **houses of worship**; "Hades Havonic Arena Monastery."

***   ***   ***

AUTHOR'S NOTE : The Covert Chapters in the life of Panther X will be written as trilogies...
*Example...Covert Chapters 1, 2, & 3 are entitled...Monrovia Spaceport Metropolis Liberia 7076 A.D.
The secret missions of Benjamin William Snow are divided into what I call Covert Chapters. Enjoy all of Mr. Snow's adventures which will be published as a set of three paperback scripts & hardcover novels.

PANTHER X IN... Monrovia Spaceport Metropolis Liberia 7076 A. D.
This time Panther X and his team must travel to the world's most heavily populated and wealthiest Capitol City located in the country of Liberia West Africa.
Monrovia Spaceport Metropolis is a highly advance infrastructure owned solely by its **own people**, the Liberian Nationals. They have built the largest privately funded Spaceport on Earth. Citizens around the world wishing to travel to any of the 400 billion star systems of Earth's galaxy come here to enjoy it's plush hotel resorts before flying to their favorite town in outer space.

Unfortunately many visitors are kidnapped out of the rooms by Greater One Monks and are brought to the Hades Havonic Arena Monastery located in an old underground Iron Ore Mine.
Over 1600 hundred **Greater One Monks** serve as the armed guards of the **Hades Havonic Arena Monastery** protecting their Bishop from every failed covert Liberian Government attempt to bring him to his Tribunal appointment.

*Panther X in... Monrovia Spaceport Metropolis Liberia 7076 A.D. Covert Chapter One A Screenplay

Panther X in... Monrovia Spaceport Metropolis Liberia 7076 A.D. Covert Chapter Two A Screenplay

Panther X in... Monrovia Spaceport Metropolis Liberia 7076 A.D. Covert Chapter Three A Screenplay

***   ***   ***   ***   ***   ***   ***   ***   ***

Whenever the world's governments fail to hunt down their local Sons of the Greater One terrorist cells the O.G.O.F.R. Force is called upon to help. The Sons of the Greater One believe that they should **lynch** their victims, **burn** them in furnaces and **inject** many of their human prey with biological and chemical agents bringing Greater One the sacrifices he requires of them.

This **Deity** is made of ivory and pearl and is twenty feet tall. **Greater One** sits on his throne in the center of Hades Havonic Arena Hall Monastery. The throne he sits upon is built on twelve incinerators...all around the throne is twelve wooden pedestals were victims held hostage against their will are hanged until their dead. Their bodies are cast into the incinerators.

The O.G.O.F.R. FORCE AKA/ OLD GLORY OPERATION FREEDOM REIGNS is an covert intelligence agency of the United States Government which is made up of the Army, Air Force, Navy, Coast Guard and the Marines. All CIA, FBI , military personnel and nongovernmental American citizens volunteering for duty must resign their active duty status, undergo the rigorous training at **CAMP OLD GLORY** in Washington D. C.
before being selected to become an O.G.O.F.R. Force Agent.

The Old Glory Operation Freedom Reigns Force is an branch of the old Central Intelligence Agency still in operation, however its covert missions reaches out into the far corners of Earth's galaxy of **400 billion metropolis star systems**...another agency had to be created to carry out U. S. Government Operations and protecting United States interests.
Old Glory Operation Freedom Reigns Force was established in 7041 A.D. the year Benjamin William Snow was born at the Philadelphia Naval Spaceport Children's Hospital located in the clouds above South Philly...

He and his team of twelve operatives would become the most powerful and decorated of all O.G.O.F.R. Force Agents...

The O.G.O.F.R. FORCE Director of Intelligence:
Douglas Noah Michelin
an Afro-American male from "Washington D. C." **Code Name: Devine Father**

Harrison's Imaginary Library Works presents A Synopsis Collection
written by Raymond Harrison

Upcoming Paperback Screenplays and Hard Cover Novels
Coming Soon for Your Enjoyment !

Director of Covert Operations:

Naomi Ester King
an Afro-American female from "Indianapolis Indiana." **Code Name: Mother Magic**

Devine Father & Mother Magic lead the **O.G.O.P.R. Force** *and it's most decorated team of covert operatives...*

Benjamin William Snow: an African American male from "Philadelphia Pennsylvania"

Code Name: PANTHER X

Ida Monique Mars: a Greek American female from "Boise Idaho"

Code Name: Strawberri Sweet

Jennifer Hanna Johnson: an African American female from "Las Vegas Nevada"

Code Name: Black Venom

Ubah Darla Wong: an Ethiopian Chinese American female from "Manhattan New York"

Code name: Lady Lollipop

Xavier Alex Jennings: an Irish Haitian American male from "Catalina Island California"

Code Name: Lord Madagascar

Jacob Lewis Smith: a Caucasian American male from "Knoxville Tennessee"

Code Name: Sleepy the Nephilim

Jake Louis Webber: a Caucasian American male from "Dallas Texas"

Code Name: Doomsday Knight

Anna Maria Del Barrio a Venezuelan American female from "Miami Florida"

Code Name: Madame Honi

Wilma Gladys Davidson an African American French female from "New Orleans Louisiana"

Code Name: Mistress Cherri

Obadiah Robert Kenneth Goldberg a Jewish American male from "Vail Colorado"

Code Name: Sir Poltergeist

Damien Karl Chang a Chinese American male from "San Francisco California"

Code Name: Master Wrong Way

Dr. Josephine Liza Thomas an Arabian African American female from "Atlanta Georgia"

Code Name: Doctor Mercy

Dr. Zachariah Stanley Cole: a British Caucasian American male from "Helena Montana"

Code Name: Doctor Madness

Death to the Innocent will not stand...

at the hands of Panther X, Strawberri Sweet, Black Venom, Lady Lollipop, Lord Madagascar, Sleepy the Nephilim, Doomsday Knight, Madame Honi., Mistress Cherri., Sir Poltergeist, Master Wrong Way, Doctor Mercy and Doctor Madness.

Together they will rid the Earth of its darkest nightmare!

Terrorism has an enemy his name is Panther X"...Benjamin William Snow is Panther X.

Harrison's Imaginary Library Works presents A Synopsis Collection
written by Raymond Harrison

Upcoming Paperback Screenplays and Hard Cover Novels
Coming Soon for Your Enjoyment !

ANTARCTICA 5888 A.D.

A Screenplay

Anthony and Kenya

Two lovers who were married

Against there family's wish...

Death could only free them.

Two cities

One ruled by a Lord another ruled by a King

Two civilizations both at war over control over the Southern Pole... Anthony must decide to obey the words of his

terrestrial high priest **Onker Old'da** who warns him if he kill s himself and his wife instead of overthrowing his parents

and those of his wife, the **Brimstone Carriage of Doom** driven by the General of Darkness an d his 1st Lieutenant would

come for himself and Kenya. Would Anthony a mere mortal man, fail to believe an Terrestrial High Priest who hates the

way his creator *V-Kmas* made him? Would he allow Onker Old'da's hatred of himself being created part human animal

and machine taint his judgment on whither to

believe the warnings of a hypocritical Priest who hates his own Androibot Maker?

Anthony must decide if death is worth the price of his lost eternal soul which would be taken to an underwater

cemetery city off the coast of Antarctica at the bottom of the ocean floor..

WICKED WRETCHED WRAITH MEN: *Blood bath Las Vegas Style!*

A Screenplay

He believed himself to be the Finger of God,

And nothing could hold him in Area 51.

With his wife Emma and their two sons at his side

Who could stop him

Who would dare,

From his Philadelphia Grand Palace Hotel Casino Resort Suite in Las Vegas Nevada,

Adulterers would meet their judgment day

Earl Harold Paul would make them pay....

WICKED WRETCHED WRAITH MEN *Return to Maple Mary*

A Screenplay

...She promised never to leave him alone.

Her love was pure and unconditional...

but was her love enough to soften his wicked wretched heart that was filled with the

absence of Peace?

...She was his Lawful wedded wife, filled with wretched wicked power.

Harrison's Imaginary Library Works presents A Synopsis Collection
written by Raymond Harrison

Upcoming Paperback Screenplays and Hard Cover Novels
Coming Soon for Your Enjoyment !

Her husbands' Scent of Death was her attraction and obsession.

She would raise their twin sons to honor their father by following in his footsteps

but not under the guidance of Wraith Master Ammonothus the Nephilim..

...Carl Harold Paul would return to her.

She was the reason he became immortal.

His thirst to shed the blood of the Adulterers, believing himself to be the *Finger of God* and

his allegiance to Ammonothus the Wraith Man, made him come to his tragic end...

MATHUA HAVILAH IN...Ethiopia 3378 B. C.

A Screenplay

He lived in a time when the Sons of God

saw the beauty of human women.

He lived in an era where 200 Angelic Watchers of the Sky came to Earth and took hundreds of wives for themselves.

Their offspring were half-human an d angelic.

They stood sixteen-feet tall.

They were might men and women of valor, but they wanted to make the Ethiopian citizens of Havilah

Kingdom slaves.

He was the ruler and descendant of Ethiopian Kings. He was a man who would not bow his knee to Angels above or their

Nephilim Armies.

He refused see his wife Malicah and their twelve sons and daughters live in captivity,

He would place his trust in the Living Maker

of the Stars Wind and Earth...and with His mighty hand Mathua Havilah would witness his armies protected as they went

into battle. For the Living Maker poured out from His

third heaven Chariot Host of Light and storms of fire,

because King Mathua Havilah placed his unwavering trust in Him.

Author's note:

I have taken the Book of Genesis an d the Book of Enoch and created my own fantasy kingdom world.
It is a world drawn form the pages of my own imagination . It is therefore, not an accurate account of the historical
Books of Genesis and Enoch..
The Adventures of King Mathua Havilah will be told in many paperback screenplays and hardcover novels for the
enjoyment of myself and those of you who I thank now in advance, who will choose to become my life long fans!

Stay tooned..

Harrison's Imaginary Library Works presents A Synopsis Collection
written by Raymond Harrison

Upcoming Paperback Screenplays and Hard Cover Novels
Coming Soon for Your Enjoyment !

The Adventures of ANDROIBOT MAN

A Screenplay

His eyes were filled with compassion.

His heart and spirit and soul overflowed with courage.

He came far away from the Universe Songhai, the Metropolis Planetary System Onyinyechi. (pronounced own-yin-yee-chi)

Now he lives in the grey celestial clouds in a mansion in the sky above Mountain Kilimanjaro, in the sweet land Tanzania,

with his human family to save the children of the earth

from their kidnappers...

Here he comes...soaring high above the rainbows...this dark and handsome man, a Super-hero created part human ,

amphibious and machine...

Welcome to Earth,

Androibot Man!

Androibot Man Suite
Lyrics by Raymond Harrison

"Look! Look! Beg your Pardon?
Look! Look! I beg your pardon?
...just look for a moment in the sky!
Here he comes Androibot Man
I beg your pardon, just take a look
He's from the Planet Onyinyechi System!

Look in the grey clouds somewhere in the rainbows, you'll find him living...with his human family.
Daughters, Raziya, Ona, Oni and his wife Lilly! Nana Gerda from Bamberg and her son Godwin and his Saint Bernards
Abednego, Shadrack Meshach , too! Butler Babukar from Victoria Falls Zimbabwe...Zimbabwe...
Here he comes, in the grey clouds,
Soaring high above the rainbows
Here he comes, in the grey clouds,
Soaring high above the rainbows...Androibot Man!
The Adventures of Androibot Man!

He's from the Universe Songhai...The Adventures of Androibot Man!
He's the Universe Songhai...the Planet Onyinyechi System.---repeat 2x

Now he lives in the sky to save the children of the Earth...
Our beloved visitor from very far away! ---repeat 2x
Androibot...Androibot...Androibot...Man!
The Adventures of Androibot Man!

Child Kidnappers return on the double...those you stole from their fathers and their mothers!
You cannot hide, you'll be brought to Justice!
"Let go of our hands! Give us to Androibot Man!"---repeat 2x

Look! Look! ---repeat 3x
Here he comes...Androibot Man.
Look! Look!---repeat 3x
He's from the planet Onyinyechi System!

Now he lives in the sky to save the children of the Earth...
Our beloved visitor from very far away! ---repeat 2x

"Androibot...Androibot...Androibot...Man! The Adventures of Androibot Man!"

Upcoming Paperback Screenplays and Hard Cover Novels
Coming Soon for Your Enjoyment !

U. S. Marshal ELEANORA MARITA ROBISON Episodes

All the way from Washington D.C.

Eleanora Martha Robinson traveled to Baton Rouge Louisiana at the request of the Governor and Lieutenant Governor

to remove the Werewolf Mobsters and Vampire Gangsters.

She was not a Vampire or a Werewolf.

She did not need to be. With her beautiful dark eyes and unwavering heart of courage,

she walked in her father's footsteps and became a ruthless U.S. Marshal. She would bring Justice and Peace to the Capitol

City of Baton Rouge in the 1930's.

The Notorious Crime Boss, an immigrant from Madagascar,

was a Vampire Composer whose name was Count Gamba Babatunji.

He believed that the power and beauty of his Jazz music could set him free from being a vampire.

He led a secret life of counterfeiting the US Dollar while entertaining is guests at the Count Gamba Club.

At Count Gamba Club the Werewolf Mobsters and Vampire Gangsters danced the night away to the Count Gamba

Babatunji tunes.

Eleanora would be accompanied by her fellow U.S. Marshal,

the dark and lovely Madelyn Miriam Wilson. These two very mortal but lovely women of the silver star would bring the

Werewolf Mobsters and Vampire Gangsters to prison for the rest of their un-natural lives!

PHILADELPHIA PALACE GRAND LAS VEGAS NEVADA USA.

This is the story of Composer Leon Woodrow Whitman.

A Screenplay

The story of the man and his music that would not die.
He created out of his imagination a Hotel Resort in Nevada so that people from all over the world could hear his music and enjoy his plays performed.
This is the story of a man who built the Philadelphia Palace Grand Hotel Casino Resort.
The hotel would be built on Liberty Bell Square of off Las Vegas Boulevard.
The Liberty Bell would stand 5 stories tall, it's guests would drive underneath of the giant replica of the Philadelphia Bell.
The center of the Hotel would be a replica of the Philadelphia City Hall named the Philadelphian Family Suites
The left wing of the hotel would be a replica of the Independence Hall, named Independence Hall Inn
The right wing of the hotel would be a replica of the Ben Franklin Art Museum named the Ben Franklin Family Inn.

The far right of the Hotel would be the same replica of the Art Museum, it would be named the Ben Franklin Opera House, there Composer Whitman's music would be heard by the Ben Franklin Opera House Orchestra.

The far left of the Hotel would be the same replica of the Independence Hall, it would be named the Schukyll River Imax Cinema Stadium 14 "See you favorite movies from Hollywood".
In the rear of the PPG Casino Resort would be a replica of the Betsy Ross House,
it would be named Betsy Ross Family Suites.
Beneath the PPG Casino Resort would be a shopping mall. It would be named the Delaware River Plaza. There would be three bridges that would take guests to the Plaza as they walked above the Delaware River crossing the Betsy Ross Bridge, the Walt Whitman Bridge or the Ben Franklin Bridge. In the replica of the Delaware canoe rides would take loved ones through the Plaza in the underground manmade water way.

Welcome to Las Vegas Nevada! Welcome to the Phildelphia Palace Grand Hotel Casino Resort!

Author's Note: Someday I hope to build this Hotel in Las Vegas Nevada and use the revenue to fund my motion pictures!

ACKNOWLEGEMENTS

To my only brother and fellow artist Steven, my sisters Ruth and Susan, thank you for the unconditional love you always gave to me ever since we were children. Susan, thanks again for your words spoken by you a long time ago..."Leave the pain of your life behind you in the year that it happened!"

To my mother Mary Agnes and my father Raymond Sr. thank you for bringing me into this world, so I could grow up to entertain all those in the coming decades who will choose to become my life long fans!

Below are the following artists I dream of working with in the coming years...

To Russell J. Bowden II, Screenwriter
and Actress Kristin Quinn (The Glorious Star & Goddess of my upcoming Movies)

Without your helpful insights and corrections,
this work it would not be a pleasure to enjoy!

My fans and I Thank you!

To Tanya Friedlinghaus, Director,
Thank you for believing in this horrid tale of fiction. Someday soon I hope to hire you to direct the motion pictures I will produce, write and score.

To G. Stubbs, Director "With or Without You" on DVD
Thank you for supporting my artistic ambitions with your encouragement and your helpful insights on the way movies should be made..."not too long-like this script"

To William Wells, Writer Director,
Thank you for your friendship. May America truly enjoy and fall in love with your cinema dreams.

To Kadeem Hardison, Actor "A Different World" Sitcom
Thank you for using your eyes of faith, for believing in my "small beginning"...I hope to hire you to play the lead in my upcoming Mount Harrison Pictures Studios'
"Super-Hero Action/Adventure...ANDROIBOT MAN!"

May your Hollywood Star shine forever in all of our hearts!

Thank you my Heavenly Father,
for the talent that you have given to me and for the opportunity to express my talent through, my work of Art and Discipline!

RAYMOND

Wicked Wretched Wraith Men :
Earl Harold Paul Immortal Man

HARRISON

A Screenplay
Book Seven

Mount Harrison Pictures Studios Press

Raymond Harrison
Copyright (c) 2006
6th Draft Published by
Mount Harrison Pictures Studios Press
www.enjoyraymondharrison.com
Visit Today!

CAST OF CHARACTERS

(Order of Appearance)

A C T   1

Men *(voice over)*
Narrator *(voice over)*
Tim Hayes
Bob Knoll
Earl Harold Paul "Immortal Man"
Abner Ivan Van Holt
James Townsend
Abner Ivan Van Holt
James Townsend
Aunt Charlotte Ann
Margaret Madison
Maple Mary Paul
Wayne Mickey Madison "U.S. Marshal"
Darlene Bainbridge "The Hymn Composer"
Anna Mae "Sister of Maple Mary"
Nancy Vivian Van Holt "U.S. Marshal"
Franklin Cartwright Hayes "U.S. Marshal"
Oscar Preston Knoll "U.S. Marshal"
Dugald De Witt Hopper Mayor of Buffalo
James Jasper Jenkins Police Commissioner
Reverend Thomas Henry Bainbridge "Darlene's Father"
Earl Harold Paul Sr. "Earl's Father"
Martha Margaret Wilson-Paul "Earl's Mother"
Earl's Supporters/Crowd
Peter "the guard"
Sister Victoria Connie York-Bainbridge "Darlene's Mother"
Vincent Royce "Captain of SS Ammonothus"
Jeremiah Peterson "Professor of Archeology"
Anna Bella "Italian Dancer/undercover U.S. Marshal"
Ammonothus "The Wraith Man"
Parents of Ammonothus: Ammontai & Haggai

A C T   2

Davey Sands
Emma Peterson
Gloria the Guard
Luther the Foreman
Agnes Anna Applegate "the reporter media-mogul"
Charles Judas Gibbons "the butler"
Mr. Paul's Children 6 boys and 7 girls
Manny "the servant"
Jacob Peterson "Emma's husband"
Judith Edith Hopkins "Jacob's lover"
Peterson Children: Billy, Samantha and Lisa
Anita Cruz "Detective of Buffalo PD"
Lawrence Williams "Detective of Buffalo PD husband of Agent Carla"
Roger Mickey Madison "FBI Agent"
Nigel Oscar Knoll "FBI Agent"
Felix Franklin Hayes "FBI Agent"
Carla Vivian Holt-Williams "FBI Agent"
Nathan "the waiter"
Minister of Buffalo Methodist Cathedral of Mercy
Little Boo Boo "Emma's unborn baby"
Unborn Baby Boys "clones of Boo Boo" *(voice over)*
Jethro Hopper
Wesley "Mr. Hopper's employee"
FBI Agent *(voice over)*

A C T   3

Angelic Beings
Captain Howard "Applegate News" helicopter pilot
Young Earl (10 years old)
Young Darlene (9 years old)
Earl's Employees (Immortal Men)
Citizens of Buffalo
TV Director
Prison Guard 1
Prison Guard 2

Wicked Wretched Wraith Men

Written by Raymond Harrison
Copyright (C) 2006
6th draft revision
raymondharrisonscript@yahoo.com

FADE IN: **WICKED WRETCHED WRAITH MEN EARL HAROLD PAUL IMMORTAL MAN BOOK SEVEN**

Main title fills the screen. The audience is listening to Raymond Harrison's Main Title Theme performed by the Mount Harrison Pictures Studio Orchestra. As text "THE OVERTURE" appears on screen vocalist performs the Wicked Wretched Wraith Men Suite.

FADE TO BLACK:

THE OVERTURE

DISSOLVE TO:

1 <u>EXT. DOWNTOWN BUFFALO NEW YORK 1885 (MINIATURE)</u>   1 --
NIGHT

Aerial view of the partially residential and business section of Buffalo with the river Niagara in the distance. In the autumn full moon light the firmament above shines brightly as **CAMERA TRAVELS** over the illuminated rooftops and windows of gas lantern lights moving swiftly toward the Park. Men are HEARD chanting.

                    MEN (V.O.)
          Adulterer you'll die, die, die.
          Your dirty rotten tongue is filled
          with lies. Cut, cut, cut. I'll cut
          your tongue, so you won't taste,
          taste, taste, taste. The ravishing
          flavor, of another man's wife.

Tiny lantern lights are seen in the distance in the wooded tree line near the falls.

DISSOLVE TO:

2 <u>EXT. NIAGARA FALLS PARK 1885 AUTUMN (MINIATURE)</u>   2 --
CONTINUOUS

The SOUND of raging waters fill the air. The wind carries orange and brown leaves through the wooded tree line along the Niagara River, while through the thick moonlit fog, men hold lanterns. The people's faces are but shadows in the rays of the full moon and cannot be clearly seen. As we approach the park, **CAMERA TRAVELS** around and through several trees whose branches give way making a path as it descends losing its velocity moving slowly. The illuminated lantern lights grow brighter in the fog. Men surround their leader while a woman stands by, watching her lover's tongue being ripped and torn out of his throat with a knife.

As his men continue chanting their **Death Song** repeatedly, more victims throats are cut quickly.

> NARRATOR (V.O.)
> Long before he became a Wraith, he
> and his wicked wretched men put to
> death every adulterer they could
> find, chanting their death song as
> they ripped open the sinners' throats
> cutting out their tongues. The
> accused would never again taste the
> sweetness of another man's wife.
> His violent exploits attracted ancient
> hybrids, angelic human warriors called
> Nephilim and not the Angels of Heaven.
> He was a courageous executioner.

In the lantern lights, with perspiration and blood, EARL'S face shines. Clearly visible in the crowd of shadows, his eyes are tearful. His mouth quivers.

> NARRATOR (V.O.) (CONT'D)
> His passion brought forth judgment
> not by God's hand, but by his own
> hand. He wept, as Jesus wept although
> he never claimed to be the Lamb of
> God. He was indeed a self-righteous
> fanatic, a crusader. His name was
> Earl Harold Paul.

With one hand he holds a fist full of tongues and a blood soaked knife. With lifted hands soiled with vomit and saliva in the foggy full moon, with River Niagara falling beneath him, his men stand proudly beside him on a rock bed cliff.

FADE OUT:

FADE IN:

3 <u>EXT. NIAGARA FALLS PARK -- DAY</u>   3

Buffalo, New York 1899 October

Twenty trash wagons pulled along by horses with the company insignia "Earl Harold Paul Waste Management Company" travel along the cobblestone streets lined with trees. Niagara Falls is in the distance. EARL HAROLD PAUL is 45 years old and well built. He walks along the side of a wagon with a pitch fork. His employee and best friend JAMES TOWNSEND a 50 year old former farmer now foreman of the company walks beside EARL.

EARL'S employees TIM HAYES age 24 and BOB KNOLL age 26 bring their fellow co-worker ABNER IVAN VAN HOLT age 35 against

his will before JAMES and himself. With his knife BOB pokes
ABNER'S head.

> TIM HAYES
> Mr. Paul! Mr. Townsend? We found
> another wretched one. This time
> he's one of our own.

> BOB KNOLL
> Here he is, Abner Ivan Van Holt!
> Adulterer you'll die, die, die!

EARL grabs him by the throat slamming him against a tree
while JAMES, BOB and TIM restrain him.

ABNER stares at EARL, BOB and TIM. Then he weeps. He
trembles. He takes a breath. He swallows hard. He sticks
out his tongue, mocking EARL and his friends.

> EARL HAROLD PAUL
> Your dirty rotten tongue-is it filled
> with lies? Confess! Tell me the
> truth? Don't lie. Don't you lie to
> me. Bob's wife? Sweet and ravishing
> she was to you?

BOB hands his knife to JAMES who gives it to EARL.

> ABNER IVAN VAN HOLT
> Sir, how long have you known me?

> EARL HAROLD PAUL
> Three years you've worked for me.

> ABNER IVAN VAN HOLT
> Three years. I've never lied to
> you, have I?

> EARL HAROLD PAUL
> No Abner. You've never have and today
> would not be a good day to start.

Earl turns his head for a moment from ABNER'S face when he
takes a whiff of the rum coming from his mouth.

> EARL HAROLD PAUL (CONT'D)
> You're intoxicated right now, very
> intoxicated...

EARL smiles. ABNER smiles back then suddenly he stops
smiling. ABNER closes his eyes for a moment then opens them
wide to reveal his tears as he begins to confess.

                    ABNER IVAN VAN HOLT
          I'm madly intoxicated with Bob's
          wife. So very, very close I was to
          her. Her scent, I still smell.
          Never, shall I forget her scent. I
          shall never ever forget her sweet
          scent.

EARL begins to weep. EARL cuts off ABNER'S nose.

                    EARL HAROLD PAUL
          Now! What can you smell, Abner Ivan
          Van Holt? I know I pay you enough.
          You could have went to the island,
          the wanton island of Manhattan and...
          and with what I pay you, you could
          have quenched your sinkin' lustful
          thirst all night. It would have
          been just your secret. The scent of
          a harlot would have been just your
          secret, not the scent of another
          man's wife.

                    ABNER IVAN VAN HOLT
          What if the harlot was married,
          Mr.Paul? What if the whore was
          already married?

EARL cuts ABNER'S throat. With towels they clean his hands
and give him new clothes as they have done countless times
before. They dump VAN HOLT'S body on to the wagon. He smiles
nodding his head yes and then no while walking closer towards
the falls beside MR. TOWNSEND.

                    EARL HAROLD PAUL
          Niagara Falls! I love this place.
          I'm glad I was born here and not
          anywhere else. Have you ever seen
          the Falls of Victoria?

                    JAMES TOWNSEND
          Zimbabwe, Africa. I've never been
          there. I have an English cousin
          named Vincent Royce. He is a Merchant
          Marine Captain. He commands the
          twenty-one sail cargo vessel-the SS
          Ammonothus. According to his last
          letter his ship has been at the Hudson
          for a week already.

                    EARL HAROLD PAUL
          I'd love to visit that part of the
          world; to see with my own eyes the
                         (MORE)

                    EARL HAROLD PAUL (CONT'D)
          beauty of an African waterfall. I
          work too much. I kill too much.

                    JAMES TOWNSEND
          Take Maple Mary aboard the Ammonothus.
          I'll send word to my cousin that
          you're coming. You can't hide from
          your father in-law forever.

EARL and JAMES smile a little. EARL nods his head.

                    EARL HAROLD PAUL
          Good. What would you do and how
          would you react if you caught your
          wife kissing another man?

                    JAMES TOWNSEND
          I'd take his rotten stinking tongue
          out and feed it to my two Black German
          Wolf Shepherds and then let them
          wash it down with warm goat's milk.
          My cousin? She's been ravished?
          That's what I've been hearin'.

                    EARL HAROLD PAUL
          Don't know James.

                    JAMES TOWNSEND
          Find out Earl.

                    EARL HAROLD PAUL
          You know I will.

                    JAMES TOWNSEND
          If Professor Jeremiah Peterson from
          that wanton island city, touched
          Maple Mary, his whole family must
          die, cause there just ain't no
          tellin', there's bound to be another
          adulterous kin of his just waiting
          to fulfill his wanton ways, with
          someone else's wife.

                    EARL HAROLD PAUL
          Who can really tell or know for sure
          how wanton a man's heart really is
          but if that Professor's lips have
          ever touched my Maple Mary, it will
          just be him dealing with only me.
          Sure wouldn't want to touch your
          pretty wife!

> JAMES TOWNSEND
> Not if you want to keep both of your
> hands from being thrown away with
> the garbage in this wagon.

> EARL HAROLD PAUL
> Or eaten by your German Wolf
> Shepherds!

They both smile at one another.

> EARL & JAMES
> In a bowl of warm goats milk!

4 INT. ESTATE OF WAYNE & MARGARET MADISON DINING ROOM   4

MAPLE MARY a 26 year old brunette Geography student, is seated
with her aunt CHARLOTTE ANN a 55 year old, ANNA MAE her 23
year old blond sister and her mother MARGARET a 58 year old.
Her father is 68 years old WAYNE MICKEY MADISON, a US Marshal.

Along with other woman kin folk are girl friends who are
sitting around the table having a birthday brunch for MAPLE
MARY. Each of the brunch guests are drinking a tall glass
of milk with their meal. CHARLOTTE ANN takes a drink of her
milk. It quenches her thirst so she takes another sip.

> CHARLOTTE ANN
> Maple Mary? Happy Birthday. Here's
> your present. It's an Egyptian
> antiquity from Cuba Wood Gun Shop.
> It was on display when I saw it
> through the window.

> MARGARET MADISON
> Charlotte what on earth were you
> doing, going down there to that old
> nasty gun shop? You like Cuba is
> that what it is?

> CHARLOTTE ANN
> Stop prying, sister! Cuba isn't
> married and Harry is in the presence
> of our Lord. God rest his soul.
> Open up your present Maple Mary!

MAPLE MARY opens the handmade crocodile case with a key.

> MAPLE MARY
> Look everyone. Thank you Aunt
> Charlotte. I wonder what Professor
> Jeremiah would say to my archeological
> find.

WAYNE reaches for the knife. MAPLE MARY hides it from him
in her arms.

> WAYNE MICKEY MADISON
> Jeremiah or your husband Earl? Why
> do you enjoy fanning the flames of
> that Manhattan Professor's heart?

5 INT. BUFFALO METHODIST CATHEDRAL OF MERCY CHAPEL -- DAY 5

EARL is seated in the second row from the front. It is the
same row he sat in as a young boy. He is nodding his head
yes and then no. He is shivering. He is weeping.

DARLENE BAINBRIDGE is the Pastor's daughter. She sits with
him. EARL suddenly lays down in the pew resting his head on
her lap like they use to do when they were kids. He raises
his feet resting them on the pew.

> DARLENE BAINBRIDGE
> What's wrong. Did you kill again?

> EARL HAROLD PAUL
> You're the only one I can trust.
> Can't trust my wife, the harlot.
> Yes I can. No. Yes, no I cannot
> trust Maple Mary. Maple Maple Mary
> my sweet wife. She's a whore.

> DARLENE BAINBRIDGE
> Stop. Stop it. Calm down. Relax!
> You're shivering Earl.

> EARL HAROLD PAUL
> Darlene, how can you come to Parish?
> I can never forgive our parents.
> For what they did to us, when we
> were little.

> DARLENE BAINBRIDGE
> That was such a long time ago.

> EARL HAROLD PAUL
> I remember like it was yesterday. I
> only come here so I can feel the
> warmth of your friendship.

He allows his tears to flow.

> EARL HAROLD PAUL (CONT'D)
> I need it now more than ever.
> Darlene.

                    DARLENE BAINBRIDGE
I do admire you. So do all my
girlfriends I talk to. Especially
the women members of this Parish
who, like myself, are glad you're
ripping out all those lying tongues.
Those no good. Well, see I must
repent to God this moment. Forgive
me oh Lord for my wretched and wicked
thoughts.

                    EARL HAROLD PAUL
Help me Darlene. Help me stay sane.

                    DARLENE BAINBRIDGE
Your choices, my sweet Earl, are
causing you to lose your mind. Your
exploits although are most
appreciated. Well, they're evil!
You may just be the one all of the
principalities and rulers of the
dark ages of time may seek after.

She wipes his eyes with her hair and hands.

                    DARLENE BAINBRIDGE (CONT'D)
Your violence attracts the Wicked
Wretched Wraiths that dwell in
darkness.

                    EARL HAROLD PAUL
If I was a Wraith, I'd make every
adulterer in the Union fall to their
knees in fear. This Northern American
continent would be free from the sin
of adultery. The women of this young
country of ours would praise me.

6 EXT. DARLENE BAINBRIDGE HOME -- NIGHT   6

DARIUS SAUL ALEXANDER is a merchant marine seaman. He is
dressed in his Captain's uniform attire. Two voluptuous
women dressed in their bedroom gowns sit in the carriage.
The driver dressed in seaman's uniform holds the door open
for him.

                    DARLENE BAINBRIDGE (V.O.)
When my husband Darius Saul Alexander
was alive...

DARIUS runs out of the house. He trips as DARLENE looks
through the window. She opens the door to the porch as he
gets up. He kicks the tree stump he fell over and climbs
into the carriage.

The ladies laugh and kiss him as he buries his head in their cleavage. The driver of the carriage drives away into the foggy moonlight while DARLENE walks on to the porch. She sits down in a squeaky rocking chair.

> DARLENE BAINBRIDGE (V.O.) (CONT'D)
> He would sneak off at night with women who came to visit him. While waiting for him to return, I'd sit on the porch.

While rocking herself in her chair, she wipes her tearful eyes. In the distance the lantern lit carriage disappears in the fog under the rays of the moon. The wind carries the laughter of DARIUS and his lovers. An unworldly sound of angelic human hybrids called wraiths crying in agony, she hears in the trees to her left. Startled, she looks up and sees their hideous faces that seem to disappear in the fog.

> DARLENE BAINBRIDGE (V.O.) (CONT'D)
> I could hear the horrid cries of the principalities of darkness that rule this town. It's their oppression that causes men to leave their beloved wives and fulfill their lustful appetites. Edgar Allan Poe or Jules Verne could have never imagined to write about what I've seen with my very own eyes. That is why, ever since I was a little girl, I've been composing Hymn Suites. Music of our Lord. Melodies that bring to my inner mind hope and strength against the wicked wretched powers of evil.

She leaves the porch walking in the direction of the sound up in the trees. She sees glowing red eyes and a hideous reptile creature walking through the fog.

7 EXT. WOODED TREE LINE PROPERTY OF DARLENE & DARIUS --   7 CONTINUOUS

Lanterns grace her porch and each window of her white Victorian home. Two possums run across the porch. They go inside the house through a hole in the screen door. While DARLENE walks further away from her home in the distance the possums scurry out of the house through the screen door and run off the porch into the wooded tree line in her direction.

Walking past a tree, a raccoon runs by her feet but she is unafraid. She walks further into the woods. To her right, a dark half boar half-man beast creature runs past her while staring at her. All around her the sounds of evil, unworldly spirits fill her ears.

She is not frightened as she finds herself surrounded by six half-man, half boar looking beasts with glowing red eyes standing five feet from her.

                    DARLENE BAINBRIDGE (V.O.)
               Alone out in the woods behind my
               home,

The beasts stand 16 feet tall looking down on her. They disappear slowly. They reappear ten feet away standing only 6 feet tall. They reappear fifteen feet away standing only 3 feet tall.

                    DARLENE BAINBRIDGE (V.O.) (CONT'D)
               Still I hear the wicked spirits,
               their howling sounds of terror so
               loud in my ears. I am not afraid of
               them for I know God is with me.

The beasts stand in the fog. As the fog passes around them they quickly vanish in the rays of the full moon.

                              DISSOLVE TO:

**8 INT. BUFFALO METHODIST CATHEDRAL OF MERCY CHAPEL --   8
MOMENTS LATER**

A tear from her eye falls on EARL'S forehead. He reaches up and wipes the tear from her eye while still laying in the pew with his head on her lap.

                    DARLENE BAINBRIDGE
               Earl? The wicked wretched powers of
               those wraiths in darkness I saw are
               real. Wake up from your crusades of
               retribution upon the lustful men of
               this town. Leave the wages of their
               sin to God. He'll make them pay.
               God never asked you to make the sinful
               men of Buffalo pay for all of their
               transgressions.

                    EARL HAROLD PAUL
               There was a time I would be so afraid
               to rest my head in your lap.

                    DARLENE BAINBRIDGE
               What can our parents do to us that
               they have not done already?

                    EARL HAROLD PAUL
               After the loss of your husband, how
               are you and your three sons?

                    DARLENE BAINBRIDGE
My sons? Oh they are wonderful.
They want to grow up to become US
Marshals like your father-in law.
Their father who was a Merchant Marine
Captain, had just returned to America
from one of his many voyages, when
he died mysteriously on island of
Manhattan. He wouldn't stop his
wanton ways. His sins got the best
of him and without your acts of
violence against his life. No tellin'
how he would have died if you would
have caught up with him.

                    EARL HAROLD PAUL
Why did you change your name back to
Bainbridge?

                    DARLENE BAINBRIDGE
I don't allow myself to be called
after him anymore. I kept my maiden
name. My life, what would it have
been like if only I would have married
you instead. I would sing to you my
praises, both by day and all through
the night. My soul would be yours
and I would never share my love with
another. How can Maple Mary hurt
you so?

                    EARL HAROLD PAUL
I remember when you use to sing to
me your Hymn Suites. So soothing.
Peaceful. Your songs were the only
ones I would allow myself to sing,
when we were kids.

                    DARLENE BAINBRIDGE
Oh Earl. And you married Maple Mary
anyway.

                    EARL HAROLD PAUL
I didn't think myself worthy of your
love. My love for you was childhood
love. How could I have loved such a
wonderful woman such as you?

                    DARLENE BAINBRIDGE
So you did have love for me after
all?

                    EARL HAROLD PAUL
          I don't know. I've known you all my
          life. Sing to me Darlene. Sing to
          me the way you use to when we were
          kids.

He smiles. She smiles back.

                    EARL HAROLD PAUL (CONT'D)
          I remember holding your hand when I
          was just a little boy on our way to
          this very church. I was just about
          ten years old.

                    DARLENE BAINBRIDGE
          But now you're not a little boy.
          You're a full grown man. My sweet,
          mysterious childhood friend you'll
          always be. No matter how many men
          you kill, I promise I will never
          stop being your friend.

She smiles. He smiles back.

                    DARLENE BAINBRIDGE (CONT'D)
          You're stuck with me, forever. I
          shall never ever leave you alone
          Earl Harold Paul.

He closes his eyes. She watches him fall asleep in her lap.
She picks up a hymnal and sings one of her published songs.

                    DARLENE BAINBRIDGE (CONT'D)
          My Matchless Lord of hope. In me
          you'll forever reign. In Your arms
          there's forgiveness left for me. In
          Your arms if I only believe. How
          can I go on and deny the power of
          Your love so divine. In Your arms
          there's forgiveness left for me. In
          Your arms if I only believe. My
          Matchless Lord of hope. My Matchless
          Lord of hope. You are. You are.
          My Lord of hope. Lord of hope.

                                        FADE OUT:

FADE IN:

9 EXT. ESTATE OF WAYNE & MARGARET MADISON DINING ROOM --   9
MOMENTS LATER

Through the window pane MAPLE MARY and her family dine while
discussing her husband.

Two squirrels run across the window sill. They stop and
look inside. MAPLE MARY smiles seeing them outside of the
window as she talks with her father.

>   MAPLE MARY
>   Honestly, father I don't flirt that
>   much. Anyway, I am busy with school.
>   Earl is such a good man letting me
>   complete my education in Manhattan
>   island.

>   WAYNE MICKEY MADISON
>   Where is Earl now, Maple Mary? I
>   need to talk to him.

>   MAPLE MARY
>   He's working.

>   WAYNE MICKEY MADISON
>   No he is not working. He's hiding.

>   MAPLE MARY
>   From who?

>   WAYNE MICKEY MADISON
>   From me. He's hiding from the
>   shinning silver Star on this leather
>   vest I'm wearing.

10 INT. ESTATE OF WAYNE & MARGARET MADISON DINING ROOM -- 10
CONTINUOUS

More squirrels join the two on the window pane. They all
scurry climbing up the side of the wooden window pane to the
rooftop. ANNA MAE startled a little looks over at MAPLE
MARY. They both smile. MAPLE MARY rests her hand on ANNA
MAE'S hand to comfort her.

>   ANNA MAE
>   You believe in all those evil rumors
>   about Earl. He's mysterious. Maple
>   Mary loves mysterious men.

>   MAPLE MARY
>   Earl may be mysterious but he is
>   certainly no Jeremiah Peterson.
>   Jeremiah says...

>   WAYNE MICKEY MADISON
>   You mean Professor Peterson, your
>   teacher of Archeology in Manhattan?

MAPLE MARY
Yes! Professor Jeremiah Peterson.

DISSOLVE TO:

11 **INT. AMMONOTHUS ANCIENT TRANSPORT TOMB SITE -- DAY** 11

Rays of Egyptian sunlight invade the cave where JEREMIAH
PETERSON, a tall British American, massages the outside of a
machine that rests on a gold and limestone pathway. He shakes
the dust from his blond hair and pulls a map from his safari
shorts. The limestone tunnel walls had fossils of giant
Nephilim men and women with wings preserved in the limestones.
The tunnel dead ends into a sulfur stone wall surrounded by
lanterns. Standing by the machine, he holds up an 1899 map
vision. JEREMIAH sits down inside of the machine that starts
to hover down the tunnel. The machine passes through the
sulfur stone wall.

MAPLE MARY (V.O.)
He's discovered in the land of Egypt
some sort of a transport carriage.

Traveling past the continent of Africa and the Indian sea.
He passes by New Zealand. Japan. Australia. To Antarctica.
The machine takes JEREMIAH inside a blue ice tunnel. Sunlight
from the surface illuminates the machine's icicled pathway.

MAPLE MARY (V.O.) (CONT'D)
He told me that this machine hovered
him quickly through a tunnel that
still exists in another dimension
from Cairo to an Antarctic Temple.

His journey ends at the Temple Tomb of Ammonothus. He sees
the sixteen-foot angelic human hybrid dressed like a warrior
in crocodile and alligator skins holding a sword standing by
the stone columns with carvings of Nephilim skulls.

DISSOLVE TO:

12 **INT. ESTATE OF WAYNE & MARGARET MADISON DINING ROOM --** 12
CONTINUOUS

WAYNE looks down at his time piece on a chain in his vest
pocket. He takes his napkin and cleans the face of his silver
plated watch before putting it back into his vest pocket.

WAYNE MICKEY MADISON
So, it's a time traveler. Our
government has been working on such
a foolish contraption. It's suppose
to be a secret.
(MORE)

                    WAYNE MICKEY MADISON (CONT'D)
          It's silly if you ask me. So your
          Professor has found an ancient time
          traveler?

                    MAPLE MARY
          Father, don't be silly! It's not a
          time traveler but some sort of
          carriage, a Model T, sort of, like
          Mr. Ford's invention. A carriage
          that only travels down a tunnel that
          exists in another dimension and with
          one destination. The Temple Tomb of
          a giant man who can shape shift.

Her family is perplexed.

                    MAPLE MARY (CONT'D)
          He could make his strong spine and
          muscles turn into the wings of a
          giant hawk.

The women laugh.

                    ANNA MAE
          That's my sister. Always thinking
          about another man.

                    MAPLE MARY
          Jeremiah called him the Wraith Man.
          He stands sixteen feet. This beastly
          hybrid was born in the days of Enoch.

                    ANNA MAE
          Another man.

The women chuckle.

                    MAPLE MARY
          The Watchers of the sky slept with
          human women.

                    ANNA MAE
          First it was Earl a mysterious would
          be killer. You married him. Then
          it was skinny Professor Peterson.

                    MAPLE MARY
          Jeremiah.

                    ANNA MAE
          Now it's a giant man. A giant.
                         (MORE)

                    ANNA MAE (CONT'D)
          My darling sister, your fantasies
          have come to the Nephilim. They've
          been extinct for centuries.

                    MAPLE MARY
          Sister? Anna Mae you don't believe
          me?

                    ANNA MAE
          You are serious. Does this fantasy
          giant man of yours have a name?

                    MAPLE MARY
          Yes. His name is Ammonothus.

Silence fills the breakfast brunch. Then Anna Mae breaks
the silence. "Hamming it up" she speaks as if she were in a
Broadway melodrama stage play in Times Square.

                    ANNA MAE
          The Wraith Man!

The women chuckle some more. Maple Mary continues ignoring
her sister's mockery.

                    MAPLE MARY
          The Professor has met him. He says
          he seeks out some one who he can
          work his evil power through.

                    ANNA MAE
          And now you wish to meet him.

MAPLE MARY'S eyes say yes as she takes a breath and she tries
to hide her infatuations for such a creature.

                    MAPLE MARY
          What on earth would I do with a wicked
          wretched man like Ammonothus?

                    WAYNE MICKEY MADISON
          You married one. What are you doing
          with the wicked wretched man you
          married?

                    MARGARET MADISON
          Making him jealous. Child? What do
          you think our Lord thinks of you and
          your silly little dreams? Besides,
          you'll make Earl so jealous of your
          admiration for Professor Peterson,
          one day you'll pay for it.
                        (MORE)

MARGARET MADISON (CONT'D)
I want you to leave your infatuations
alone. If I realized Earl Harold
Paul was such a dangerous man you
would have never married him. I
would not have allowed it.

WAYNE MICKEY MADISON
Although he's never been caught,
yet, he kills adulterers of this
town. I admire him. I do. That's
why I allowed you to marry him. I
have no proof he's killed, but he
surrounds himself with his fanatic
followers. When mother and I first
met him, we thought he was heaven
sent. A man of great morality. Now
I fear his heart is completely filled
with iniquity.

MARGARET MADISON
We love you Maple Mary. But you
need to live somewhere else. Take
him far away from Buffalo, before he
is killed. He is your husband for
life, for better or worst!

WAYNE MICKEY MADISON
He's no aristocrat but he works hard
on keeping this town clean, not filthy
like the island of Manhattan. I'm
sure you two can find a life of your
own somewhere else. It may be noble
to clean the cobble streets of Buffalo
of the wanton and lustful men by
killing them. Well. Murder still
has a price. At the US Marshal's
office we think he might be linked
to the murder of Federal Court Judge
Van Hauser. My partner thinks he
may have had a hand in the murder of
her brother Abner Van Holt.

MARGARET MADISON
I am sorry Maple Mary but you need
to go away with your husband before
your father kills him.

MAPLE MARY
You want to kill my husband. Over
what father?

                    MARGARET MADISON
          You father just told you. He is a
          highly respected US Marshal. Just
          how long can he withhold power given
          to him by President William McKinley
          to arrest all violators of the law?
          Earl Harold Paul is not an immortal
          man. He can not travel through the
          centuries of time and kill every
          adulterer he finds.

                    WAYNE MICKEY MADISON
          He cannot escape the judgment of his
          actions. The US Marshal's office
          here in Buffalo will bring him to
          justice and if he is convicted he'll
          hang.

                    MAPLE MARY
          Earl Harold Paul is my husband and
          my husband is no murderer!

                    MARGARET MADISON
          Maple Mary, your father just doesn't
          want to be the one to kill him because
          he is your husband, our son-in law.

                    WAYNE MICKEY MADISON
          Happy birthday my love, and many
          more to come.

He hands her a copy of Jules Verne's *Journey to the Center
of the Earth.* With tears in her eyes she accepts the gift.

                    MAPLE MARY
          Where ever Earl will take me I'll
          follow. Thank you father. You know
          how I love Jules Verne.

                    ANNA MAE
          Yet another man.

MAPLE MARY wipes her tears away smiling at her favorite
author's book. She looks over at ANNA MAE. With tears in
her eyes they embrace.

                    MARGARET MADISON
          On this special day.

MARGARET MADISON holds back her tears. She wishes she could
take back all the words of truth she said to her daughter
but she knows she needed to hear them for her own good.

                    MARGARET MADISON (CONT'D)
          Maple Mary may all of your wildest
          dreams come true!

                    EVERYONE
          Happy Birthday Maple Mary!

                    WAYNE MICKEY MADISON
          May none of your wildest fantasies
          come true. Not a single one.

MAPLE MARY upset at her father's last remark leaves the table
and runs up the winding Persian rug stairs to her former
childhood bedroom.

                                        DISSOLVE TO:

**13 INT. CHILDHOOD BEDROOM SUITE OF MAPLE MARY -- MOMENTS   13
LATER**

She closes the door. In her room, stuffed animals and
porcelain dolls dressed in attire representative of many
different cultures lay neatly all around. Her canopy is in
the middle of the floor. EARL is under the covers. The
window is open. The curtains blow in the wind. She closes
the windows. She notices someone in her bed. At first she
is startled but realizes it must be EARL. She runs to her
bedroom door and locks it. She jumps into bed with her
husband who allows her under the covers with him.

                                        DISSOLVE TO:

14 INT. UNDER BEDDING OF MAPLE MARY -- MOMENTS LATER   14

                    EARL HAROLD PAUL
          Remember when I used to hide in this
          very room? Remember?

                    MAPLE MARY
          I know. My darling? Why aren't you
          at work? You're here to surprise
          me?

                    EARL HAROLD PAUL
          It's your birthday! I thirst after
          you so much. Your love quenches my
          soul.

                    MAPLE MARY
          You move me so. I wish you weren't
          so poor.

                    EARL HAROLD PAUL
          I talk of love. You think of money.

>   MAPLE MARY
>   I think people may try to kill you
>   tonight. If we had money you could
>   take me away from Buffalo. I don't
>   want to hear the troubles you are
>   having with my father. I don't want
>   to know.

>   EARL HAROLD PAUL
>   No need to worry Maple Mary, I won't
>   tell you my troubles. I came not to
>   tell you my troubles but to have a
>   drink of you!

He kisses her.

>   MAPLE MARY
>   Oh my darling. Tonight. Come to
>   the ball. The Professor will be
>   there and I want you to finally meet
>   him.

>   EARL HAROLD PAUL
>   Yes we do have to leave Buffalo. We
>   have to leave this entire state of
>   New York. Here I am under the
>   bedspreads with you and you speak of
>   another man.

>   MAPLE MARY
>   Let's go away with him. You and I.

>   EARL HAROLD PAUL
>   Some say you've already been with
>   him. Intimately. Your cousin James
>   thinks this is true. Is it?

He weeps.

>   MAPLE MARY
>   No! No my darling. My cousin doesn't
>   know what he's talking about.

They kiss. She kisses his tears. He nods his head yes and
then no. She calms him down by caressing his face gently.
MAPLE MARY knows the strokes of her hand massaging his face
always seem to calm him down. It works.

EARL stops weeping.

There is a knock at the door.

>   MAPLE MARY (CONT'D)
>   Go to our house. I'll meet you there.

                    EARL HAROLD PAUL
          No! I'll be at the Methodist
          Cathedral of Mercy. Hiding, waiting
          for you.

                    MAPLE MARY
          My father and his fellow US Marshals
          are after you. Let's leave with the
          professor tonight.

                    EARL HAROLD PAUL
          The professor again?

He grabs her throat. The knock at the door is heard once
more. He whispers.

                    EARL HAROLD PAUL (CONT'D)
          Are you quenching Jeremiah Peterson's
          thirst with your tongue? Your tongue
          your body your heart is mine all
          mine. You're my pride and possession!

He has tears in his eyes and they fall on her face. Still
he has his hands around her neck. MAPLE MARY shows no fear
as she stares back at him, although she can hardly breathe.

                    MAPLE MARY
          Be my man Mr. Paul! The man I married
          has got the confidence to kill but
          not the will to trust his wife?
          Darling he doesn't know how sweet I
          taste. Jeremiah desires me deeply
          what wanton man wouldn't want to
          taste my charms but he'd never dare
          touch me!

                    EARL HAROLD PAUL
          Whore! You whore. You ask for my
          trust? Is it because you think you
          don't have it? You're my wife!

                    WAYNE MICKEY MADISON (V.O.)
          Maple Mary. Maple Mary I'm sorry.

                    EARL HAROLD PAUL
          I love you. You whore. I love you.

MAPLE MARY is losing consciousness. He stops. He realizes
he is killing her.

                    MAPLE MARY
          I love you. You murderer. I need
          you.

She grabs his throat down hard with all of her might, then
she grabs his hair forcing him to continue to kiss him.
Stunned, he resists her continued kisses.

> EARL HAROLD PAUL
> Did I marry a harlot?

She places her hands gently behind her head.

> MAPLE MARY
> Did I marry an executioner?

He releases her throat.

> WAYNE MICKEY MADISON (V.O.)
> Will you forgive your father?

> MAPLE MARY
> Yes, Father, I need some rest. I'm
> going to the Ball tonight.

> WAYNE MICKEY MADISON (V.O.)
> It's morning Love. Open this door
> at once. Is your husband in this
> room? Earl Harold Paul. Come out.
> I just want to talk to you.

> MAPLE MARY
> Earl? Go. Meet me at the Ball
> tonight. At Niagara Falls. Tonight.

15 **EXT. BEDROOM SUITE DOOR OF MAPLE MARY** -- CONTINUOUS   15

WAYNE has his head resting on the door. His wife and their
daughters are teary eyed. They stand beside him.

> WAYNE MICKEY MADISON
> I know you hear me. Leave Buffalo.
> Never return. If you do I'll kill
> you. I know you murdered the brother
> of my partner regardless if I can't
> prove it. You may have killed an
> adulterer but he was also the brother
> of a US Marshal. Get out of my house
> Earl Harold Paul and take your wife
> with you. Good bye Maple Mary.

WAYNE begins to weep.

16 **INT. UNDER BEDDING OF MAPLE MARY** -- CONTINUOUS   16

EARL, frightened, nods his head yes then no repeatedly with
tears in his eyes. MAPLE MARY caresses his face, calming
him down.

                    WAYNE MICKEY MADISON (V.O.)
          You hear me Earl Harold Paul? Take
          my daughter and leave Buffalo.
          Tonight! Never return!

Footsteps are heard walking away from the door.

                    EARL HAROLD PAUL
          Take a carriage to the Hudson Harbor
          on the island of Manhattan. See
          your cousin Captain Vincent Royce...

                    MAPLE MARY
          I have not seen my English cousin
          since Uncle Harry died and left my
          Aunt Charlotte a widow. For that
          matter I have not seen my cousin
          James. He's still working for you?

                    EARL HAROLD PAUL
          Yes. It's all been arranged. We
          are both leaving America aboard the
          SS Ammonothus. We may never return
          to America so say your good byes to
          your family. I'll meet you at Hudson
          Harbor tomorrow.

                    MAPLE MARY
          Wonderful Earl. The Professor has
          been aboard the SS Ammonothus and,

                    EARL HAROLD PAUL
          Hold your tongue and don't speak his
          name again to me. Ever!

MAPLE MARY reveals her breasts to her husband.

                    MAPLE MARY
          Shut up! Drink and get drunk. I
          know you can't get enough of my
          charms.

EARL kisses his wife's breasts ravishing her charms.

                    MAPLE MARY (CONT'D)
          Our voyage aboard the Ammonothus
          will be the greatest of all birthday
          gifts you have ever given to me.

MAPLE MARY can't hardly believe that her wildest dreams have
come true. They tear each others clothes off under the
bedding and make love.

                    EARL HAROLD PAUL
          Happy birthday Maple Mary my sweet
          wife! You're the wine of my life!

                    MAPLE MARY
          Oh! Earl. Oh, oh! Earl! You are
          the best birthday gift God has ever
          given to me. Me! Me! Me.

                                        FADE OUT:

FADE IN:

17 <u>INT. ESTATE LIBRARY OF WAYNE MICKEY MADISON</u> --SUNSET   17

In the estate library, at sunset, a secret meeting of US
Marshals is on this wise; WAYNE MICKEY MADISON, OSCAR PRESTON
KNOLL, FRANKLIN CARTWRIGHT HAYES, AND NANCY VIVIAN VAN HOLT
discuss matters of a sensitive nature.

Buffalo City Mayor DUGALD DE WITT HOPPER, Police Commissioner
JAMES JASPER JENKINS and Police Detective MANUEL MATTEO CRUZ
are on hand. Reverend THOMAS HENRY BAINBRIDGE and his wife
Sister VICTORIA CONNIE-YORK BAINBRIDGE sit quietly with the
parents of the accused, MARTHA MARGARET WILSON-PAUL and her
husband EARL HAROLD PAUL SR., giving them moral support.
Wayne's Butler, CHARLES JUDAS GIBBONS, a freed slave in his
50's, serves lemonade. EARL is still upstairs making love
to his wife. Faintly their cries of passion are heard
downstairs. The guests try to ignore it. WAYNE closes the
double doors of his library study.

                    WAYNE MICKEY MADISON
          For those who don't know my partners
          and fellow US Marshals. This is
          Oscar Preston Knoll, Franklin
          Cartwright Hayes, and Nancy Vivian
          Van Holt.

Suddenly to the comfort of WAYNE the cries of love making
ceases to be heard as he walks over to his co-workers.

                    NANCY VIVIAN VAN HOLT
          What wickedness can overpower us?

                    FRANKLIN CARTWRIGHT HAYES
          When we know that our wives-

Now to the discomfort of WAYNE the cries of love making
continues to be heard as the Marshal's motto continues.

                    NANCY VIVIAN VAN HOLT
          Or husband.

                    FRANKLIN CARTWRIGHT HAYES
Love us?

              FRANKLIN, NANCY, OSCAR, WAYNE
Nothing. Nothing. Nothing.

As WAYNE speaks, he hears the voice of EARL and MAPLE MARY.
The rest of his guests can't make out what is being said
upstairs because they're busy enjoying the US Marshal's motto!
While EARL and MAPLE MARY converse the Marshal's motto is
spoken by WAYNE and his partners simultaneously.

                  WAYNE MICKEY MADISON
We'll defend our family with our
very lives.

              FRANKLIN, NANCY, OSCAR, WAYNE
Forever!

             WAYNE MICKEY MADISON
The love we have for our wives.

                 EARL HAROLD PAUL (V.O.)
Quiet Maple Mary! There are
adulterers in this house.

               MAPLE MARY (V.O.)
Where are you going? Who are you
going to execute now?

               NANCY VIVIAN VAN HOLT
Or husband.

              WAYNE MICKEY MADISON
In our hearts.

             FRANKLIN, NANCY, OSCAR, WAYNE
Will forever reign. Reign. Reign.

               MAPLE MARY (V.O.)
You're not finished giving me your
present and it's my birthday! Come
back to bed.

                 EARL HAROLD PAUL (V.O.)
Keep your voice down!

              OSCAR PRESTON KNOLL
What evil in Buffalo, New York can
harm us-

             WAYNE MICKEY MADISON
With the love we have for our wives-

                    NANCY VIVIAN VAN HOLT
          Or husband.

                    WAYNE MICKEY MADISON
          In our hearts?

                    FRANKLIN,NANCY,OSCAR,WAYNE
          Nothing.

                    WAYNE MICKEY MADISON
          The love we have for our wives.

                    NANCY VIVIAN VAN HOLT
          Or husband.

                    FRANKLIN,NANCY,OSCAR,WAYNE
          Casts out all fear.

Mayor DUGALD DE WITT HOPPER stands to his feet while WAYNE
places both of his hands behind his back. He releases into
the palm of his right hand a pistol that is ejected from the
inside of his sleeve. Mayor HOPPER is in the line of fire
with his back facing the library double doors. WAYNE remains
calm. NANCY recognizes the gun in WAYNE'S hand behind his
back. She puts both of her hands behind her back. Two hand
pistols are released from the inside of her sleeves into the
palm of her hands.

                    DUGALD DE WITT HOPPER
          You US Marshals are indeed the
          servants of this city. And as your
          Mayor, I Dugald De Witt Hopper do
          solemnly swear to give you my full
          support. Commissioner Jenkins do
          you agree?

The Commissioner stands to his feet blocking the line of
fire with his back facing the library double doors.

                    JAMES JASPER JENKINS
          Mayor Hopper. I firmly believe that
          if these US Marshals can't stop the
          evil in the heart of Mr. Earl Harold
          Paul...

He glances over at EARL SR.

                    JAMES JASPER JENKINS (CONT'D)
          Unfortunately, your son...Our
          descendants may tragically pay the
          price for our lack of courage.

WAYNE looks at the butler. CHARLES leaves the room but
listens on the other side of the double doors of the library.

                    MARTHA MARAGARET WILSON-PAUL
          I Martha Margaret Wilson-Paul give
          you all my blessing. May the sins
          of my past be forever washed away
          from the mind and heart of my eldest
          son.

                    JAMES JASPER JENKINS
          What sins of your past?

                    REV.THOMAS HENRY BAINBRIDGE
          Her sins. Your sins. Everyone in
          this room has been forgiven for all
          their transgressions.

                    JAMES JASPER JENKINS
          I'm not much of a church-goer.

EARL HAROLD PAUL comes into the room just as CHARLES passes
him with a platter of tall glasses of freshly squeezed
lemonade. He takes a tall glass. Everyone stares at EARL.

                    EARL HAROLD PAUL
          But you are still an adulterer right?
          Commissioner James Jasper Jenkins?

EARL looks at him while drinking the entire glass of lemonade.

                    JAMES JASPER JENKINS
          I was. But my wife and God forgave
          me.

He finishes his drink and places the glass on CHARLES'S tray.
CHARLES bows his head as he enters the library behind EARL.
EARL reaches into CHARLES'S trouser white uniform jacket
pocket and takes out a kitchen knife. CHARLES whispers into
the ear of EARL.

                    CHARLES GIBBONS
          Kill the adulterers. Show no mercy.
          Cut cut cut their dirty rotten
          tongues.

EARL smiles but keeps his eye on WAYNE and his guests. He
is glad CHARLES has not failed in providing his weapon.

                    EARL HAROLD PAUL
          I don't forgive you. Your maker, if
          there's one that exists, doesn't
          forgive you, because he is weak.

EARL walks quickly over to the Commissioner. The US Marshals
draw their weapons.

                    WAYNE MICKEY MADISON
          "Guns down". Don't fire. Earl you
          wouldn't dare. Put down that knife.

He reaches the Commissioner. Grabs him. JAMES draws his
weapon "but feels" EARL'S knife go right through his throat
before he can fire off a round. He falls to the floor.

NANCY aims her hand pistols and fires. As her weapons
misfire, EARL'S mother and father quickly move in the line
of fire. Protecting their son they stand foolishly with
their backs against him. They face the US Marshals daring
them to fire their weapons. EARL grabs his father. Placing
his knife against EARL SR'S neck he begins to bleed.

                    EARL HAROLD PAUL
          Father? Confess!

                    EARL HAROLD PAUL SR.
          No! My son. You are not the Lamb
          of God. You're not his finger.
          Take my life if you wish.

EARL SR. weeps.

                    EARL HAROLD PAUL SR. (CONT'D)
          I have destroyed yours. Forgive me.

MARTHA hugs her son just as EARL slits the throat of his
father. He then grabs his mother and places the knife against
her throat. She begins to bleed.

MARTHA weeps.

                    MARTHA MARAGARET WILSON-PAUL
          I've given life to you. I have also
          taken your life away. Forgive me.
          The Lord my precious Living Maker
          has forgiven me. Cut out my tongue,
          my son, if you wish.

EARL drives the knife through his mother's throat. The entire
MADISON HOUSEHOLD enters the room. They surround EARL. The
US Marshals aim their weapons at EARL, but WAYNE'S family is
in the line of fire. EARL holds his mother who still is
embracing as she falls with her to the floor. The knife
falls out of his hand. EARL SR. and his wife embrace their
son as blood fills their lungs.

EARL HAROLD PAUL lays down over his parents and weeps.

                    WAYNE MICKEY MADISON
          Put down your weapons.
                         (MORE)

                    WAYNE MICKEY MADISON (CONT'D)
          Earl Harold Paul will be put to death
          in front of the citizens he has
          terrorized. I want every man, woman,
          boy and girl in this town to see the
          end of this wicked and wretched man!

OSCAR, NANCY and FRANKLIN apprehend EARL who continues to
hold his dying parents. WAYNE stares into the eyes of CHARLES
whose eyes are filled with tears. CHARLES most disappointed
that EARL will be put to death looks down at EARL. He looks
into the eyes of WAYNE, the man whose grandparents own his
family as slaves.

                    CHARLES GIBBONS
          Yes Master Wayne Mickey Madison?

                    WAYNE MICKEY MADISON
          You know I don't allow you to call
          me Master. My father freed your
          people.

                    CHARLES GIBBONS
          His father enslaved my people.

                    WAYNE MICKEY MADISON
          What did you whisper to Earl?

                    CHARLES GIBBONS
          I told Earl to give himself up.

                    WAYNE MICKEY MADISON
          You had a knife your pocket.

                    CHARLES GIBBONS
          I always carry kitchen utensils in
          my pocket. I clean the dishes and
          answer the door. That's my job.

                    WAYNE MICKEY MADISON
          You're fired. Get out of my house!

As more policemen enter the library they assist the US
Marshals with EARL. CHARLES GIBBONS leaves pushing the
officers out of his way. The officers take forks, spoons
and hand towels out of his uniform jacket pockets.

                    WAYNE MICKEY MADISON (CONT'D)
          Let him go. He was our dish washer
          and butler. That was his job.

                                        DISSOLVE TO:

18 **INT. POLICE CARRIAGE WAGON** -- **MOMENTS LATER**   18

EARL is carried away as the carriage rolls off the property.
The entire household stands out on the lawn. The US Marshals
ride in the rear to prevent EARL'S SUPPORTERS from getting
near the carriage jail wagon. Inside he holds the bars of
the wagon jail cell. MAPLE MARY runs behind the jail wagon
with tears in her eyes. She pushes the crowd out of her way
and reaches the moving jail wagon. She reaches through the
bars. EARL grabs her hands. The wagon slows down but does
not stop.

                    EARL'S SUPPORTERS
          Adulterers will die die die. Their
          wicked wretched tongues are filled
          with lies!

                    MAPLE MARY
          I don't care if you are an executioner
          I love you!

                    EARL HAROLD PAUL
          Do you?

                    MAPLE MARY
          You're my man! You know I worship
          you.

                    EARL HAROLD PAUL
          Then don't be my harlot wife. Just
          be my wife. My sweet wedded wife.

                    MAPLE MARY
          I am your sweet wedded wife, your
          only wife. No other man has ever
          ravished my charms. I will wait for
          you at the Manhattan Island Hudson
          Harbor Port. My soul belongs to
          you.

                    EARL HAROLD PAUL
          Help me find mine...I don't know
          where I left it.

                    MAPLE MARY
          I need you Earl Harold Paul.

                    EARL HAROLD PAUL
          Happy Birthday. Maple Mary Paul.

MAPLE MARY lets go of his hands. She covers her mouth and
weeps.

EARL'S SUPPORTERS repeat the death song chant as the carriage moves down the road and the entire town comes to greet the carriage. Many cheer while others weep for EARL. The police try to hold the crowd back as EARL smiles at his followers.

DISSOLVE TO:

19 EXT. BUFFALO POLICE JAIL HOUSE -- MOMENTS LATER   19

Protesters line the streets with EARL'S SUPPORTERS who have knives in their hands and pitch forks, holding them high as they walk down the street along side of the police wagon.

EARL listens to the crowd as his SUPPORTERS continue their chant. He smiles but weeps at the same time as the carriage jail wagon enters through the police gate.

He notices DARLENE BAINBRIDGE and her parents riding on horseback. They are permitted to enter the police courtyard property behind the jail wagon. WAYNE MICKEY MADISON and his fellow partners and other policemen dismount their horses.

EARL looks into the eyes of DARLENE who rides closer to the jail wagon. She dismounts and reaches through the bars. EARL holds her hands.

                    DARLENE BAINBRIDGE
          Place your continued trust in the
          Lord of hope, my sweet childhood
          friend.

They are separated by the police.

FADE OUT:

FADE IN:

20 INT. BUFFALO POLICE JAIL HOUSE CELL -- NIGHT   20

EARL stands behind the bars of his cell. His friend JAMES TOWNSEND, BOB KNOLL, and TIM HAYES are visiting him. Through the bars they give him a hunting knife and a sack lunch.

                    EARL HAROLD PAUL
          Gentlemen? Thanks!

                    JAMES TOWNSEND
          I've sent word to my cousin. He has
          room aboard the SS Ammonothus for
          you and Maple Mary. He's due to
          leave on Sunday from Hudson Harbor.

                    EARL HAROLD PAUL
          I've got to leave tonight. I am
          going to hang!

Acting surprised. He knows his friends will rescue him.

                    BOB,JAMES & TIM
          You're going to hang Mr. Paul?

                    EARL HAROLD PAUL
          My wicked wretched parents at last
          are dead!

EARL and his men lower their head, mocking the murders of
his parents.

                    EARL HAROLD PAUL (CONT'D)
          The old adulterous wind-bags...

                    BOB KNOLL
          God rest their wretched wicked souls!

Suddenly, EARL and his men lift their heads. JAMES, TIM and
BOB try their best to sing the Christmas tune "*God Rest Ye
Merry Gentlemen*". Same tune different words.

                    JAMES,TIM & BOB
          *"God rest! God rest their wanton
          souls! May they! May they rot in
          hell"*

                    EARL HAROLD PAUL
          "In Hell!"

EARL and his men laugh.

                    EARL HAROLD PAUL (CONT'D)
          So! Gentlemen?

                    JAMES,TIM & BOB
          Yes Earl?

                    BOB KNOLL
          We you be *a hangin'* tonight? Mr.
          Paul?

                    EARL HAROLD PAUL
          They...Will not hang me until
          tomorrow... Mr. Knoll.

EARL and his men laugh some more.

                    EARL HAROLD PAUL (CONT'D)
          Morning!

                    BOB KNOLL
So you will have to escape tonight.

                    EARL HAROLD PAUL
Good thinking! Bob.

                    BOB KNOLL
Tell the Reverend to come read the
Holy Scriptures to you.

                    TIM HAYES
When the guards open the cell you'll
have to kill the adulterous Reverend.

                    EARL HAROLD PAUL
Which was my plan anyway. May Darlene
forgive me. Meet me in the alley
beside this wall.

They grab EARL'S hand and arms as if they were Roman soldiers.
His friends become teary eyed. The joking ceases.

                    EARL HAROLD PAUL (CONT'D)
James? I may never see you again.
Give my regards to your pretty wife.
That goes for all of you. Tell your
wives and children I love them.

                    JAMES TOWNSEND
We're taking you to the island of
Manhattan tonight. Let us save our
good byes 'til then...Who knows, we
might be forced to come aboard his
majesty the Ammonothus if we can't
get there before the US Marshals. I
must remind you old friend, don't
kill Jeremiah Peterson aboard my
cousin's ship or he'll have you thrown
over board.

                    EARL HAROLD PAUL
The Professor will be on board?

                    JAMES TOWNSEND
With your wife. They just left town.
Here comes the Reverend. Leave
tonight my friend. Come back to us.
Together we will purge Buffalo of
all the adulterers!

The Reverend BAINBRIDGE and his wife comes to the cell.
EARL'S friends leave.

A guard named PETER, a black man in his 30's, seven feet
tall and muscular, opens the cell.

> PETER THE GUARD
> Earl Harold Paul? Bible study time!
> Before your hangin' in the morn'in.

PETER stays. He stands outside the cell.

> REV.THOMAS HENRY BAINBRIDGE
> Leave us Peter.

> PETER THE GUARD
> I don't rightly wanna do that Reverend
> Bainbridge.

> SIS. VICTORIA CONNIE YORK-BAINBRIDGE
> We know he's wicked and wretched.
> Leave us alone with him anyway Peter.
> Come take us out when it's over!

> PETER THE GUARD
> Excuse me, Sister Victoria?

> REV.THOMAS HENRY BAINBRIDGE
> Leave us. See you this Sunday, Peter
> at Buffalo Methodist Cathedral of
> Mercy. I'll be watching over you
> and this whole city. Run along son.

The Reverend and his wife fight to hold back their tears.

> PETER THE GUARD
> As you wish. I'll be at the front
> desk. Just holler. I'll come
> runnin'. Gettcha' two away from
> this man of iniquity. I'll leave
> the door open.

> EARL HAROLD PAUL
> Why would you leave the door open.
> Don't you know I killed my parents
> this afternoon?

> PETER THE GUARD
> I want you to escape. I want to
> kill you because you did kill both
> of your parents this afternoon. You
> have not read in the scriptures where
> is says "Honor thy father and mother
> or Peter the Guard will kill you".
> It's in my Bible. Would you care to
> read my Bible? My words are true.

                    EARL HAROLD PAUL
          Thank you Peter the Guard. Not right
          now.

PETER walks down the hall. THOMAS and VICTORIA kneel at the
feet of EARL HAROLD PAUL. He stands in front of them and he
takes out a knife from his sack lunch. They look into his
tearful eyes. He looks into their tearful eyes.

                                        DISSOLVE TO:

21 <u>INT. BUFFALO POLICE JAIL HOUSE FRONT DESK</u> -- MOMENTS   21
LATER

There's a sound of someone falling to the floor down the
hallway as DARLENE sits with PETER at his desk. They both
glance at each other and run down the hall.

There is another sound of someone else falling to the floor.
Then BOOM! The sound of diatomite. The sounds of gun fire
outside the prison walls.

22 <u>EXT. BUFFALO JAIL HOUSE ALLEY STREET</u> -- CONTINUOUS

EARL'S friends help him out the window and into a black
carriage. As they ride off DARLENE comes to the window.

                    DARLENE BAINBRIDGE
          Earl? Earl! What have you done?

She repeats those words through her tears. She tries to
pull herself together then cries in anguish. She tries to
climb out of the rubble that a moment ago was a window pane
but the drop is four stories.

23 <u>INT. BUFFALO POLICE JAIL HOUSE CELL</u> -- CONTINUOUS   23

PETER helps her down off the rubble to keep her from falling
over the side into the alley. She embraces her parents as
they embrace her. She watches them suffocate in their own
blood. DARLENE kisses the bloody mouths of her parents.

                 REV.THOMAS HENRY BAINBRIDGE
          You must forgive Earl for this!

She cries. She screams.

                    DARLENE BAINBRIDGE
          Oh. I cannot.

                 MARTHA MARAGARET WILSON-PAUL
          Turn to the power of the Lord of
          hope!
                        (MORE)

                    MARTHA MARAGARET WILSON-PAUL (CONT'D)
          That hymn...You published when you
          were such a little girl. Give your
          life to our Lord's mighty hand as I
          and your father have. Always pray
          for His mercy upon your life your
          children and Earl Harold Paul. I
          know you love him so!

DARLENE remembers her own hymn. She holds her mother and
father tighter. She allows her tears to flow and she sings
a few words from her hymn suite "Lord of hope".

                    DARLENE BAINBRIDGE
          *"How can I go on and...deny the power
          of"*...How can I forgive Earl for
          this? Mother? Father?

                    REV.THOMAS HENRY BAINBRIDGE
          Child? You are the bright hope of
          this city. Forgive me and your mother
          for all that we've done against you.

                    MARTHA MARAGARET WILSON-PAUL
          Remember, when you both were kids at
          the Cathedral of Mercy? Oh how your
          father taught about the Glory of
          Mercy. God's mercy. The Power and
          the Glory of His Forgiveness. Turn
          to His Matchless Light this night.

DARLENE'S parents die in her arms.

                    DARLENE BAINBRIDGE
          I forgive. Through my sorrow I
          forgive. With the power of the Lord
          of hope. I forgive you father and
          mother for what you did to Earl and
          I when we were children.

Tears flow from her eyes and she cries in anguish.

                    DARLENE BAINBRIDGE (CONT'D)
          I forgive you my dearest friend Earl
          Harold Paul. I forgive your wicked
          heart. I will not allow your
          wretchedness to control my mind or
          my emotions.

US Marshals WAYNE, NANCY, FRANKLIN and OSCAR enter the cell
and help DARLENE to her feet. Her tears flow down her face
as she mourns.

                                        DISSOLVE TO:

24 <u>EXT. MANHATTAN'S HUDSON HARBOR -- DAY</u>   24

The family and in-laws of EARL and MAPLE MARY say their
farewells to them. Their love for him still abides in their
hearts. They gather around him. Captain VINCENT ROYCE the
commander in his 40's walks down the ramp to greet his cousin
JAMES TOWNSEND. The family is stunned at the beauty of his
majesty, the SS Ammonothus, a cargo vessel with twenty-one
sails.

Musicians and other members of the ship's crew walk up the
ramp carrying their gear and luggage. Professor PETERSON
walks down the ramp proudly with MAPLE MARY.

Captain ROYCE boldly takes his cousin MAPLE MARY by the hand
to her family so she may say her good-byes. They embrace
her. They wave goodbye as she is escorted back up the ramp
by the Professor. EARL'S family and friends walk with him.
Some push him around and rough him up a bit. He remains
calm.

His employees separate his family from him. EARL watches
his wife and the Professor enter the sail cargo vessel.

> DARLENE BAINBRIDGE
> Earl. I want to hate you. My mind
> wants to hate you...but I resist...in
> the name of our Lord I resist hating
> you.

She pushes EARL'S men out of her way. She grabs his face
and holds it tightly in her hands. She grits her teeth.
Bites her lip a bit. Takes a deep breath. DARLENE full of
grace stands tall and maintains her composure as she talks
to him. She is the perfect lady.

> DARLENE BAINBRIDGE (CONT'D)
> My dearest friend. I see through
> this jealous rage...Your childhood
> scares, I have them too, but I will
> not let the power of Unforgiveness
> have my spirit or my future!

She cries in his arms. EARL holds her.

> EARL HAROLD PAUL
> I'm not sorry I kill both of our
> parents. They deserved to die! I
> can promise you I won't kill the
> Professor aboard the SS Ammonothus.

She weeps as she looks into his eyes standing close in his
arms face to face. She allows him to wipe the tears from
her eyes.

                    DARLENE BAINBRIDGE
          Why make death your dwelling
          place?...The wicked wretched Wraiths
          of Darkness your Masters Earl Harold
          Paul?

EARL weeps.

                    EARL HAROLD PAUL
          ...But he touched my wife! My Maple
          Mary. He ravished her charms. He
          deserves death!

                    DARLENE BAINBRIDGE
          And you killed both my parents and
          yours.

                    EARL HAROLD PAUL
          Professor Jeremiah Peterson will die
          for his sins.

                    DARLENE BAINBRIDGE
          Our Lord and Savior died for his
          sins!

                    EARL HAROLD PAUL
          ...But I am the *Finger of God!*

DARLENE cannot stop her tears from flowing.

                    DARLENE BAINBRIDGE
          I morn my parents and yours but I
          grieve for your lost soul. My mind
          says you cannot change. I don't
          believe what my thoughts tell me.

VINCENT ROYCE embraces his cousin JAMES TOWNSEND. He takes
EARL'S luggage.

                    VINCENT ROYCE
          Here, I've got it mate, let me help.

                    EARL HAROLD PAUL
          Thank you.

DARLENE won't let go of her embrace as she weeps. EARL does
his best to shake the hand of VINCENT.

                    JAMES TOWNSEND
          EARL this is my cousin from London.
          Captain Vincent Royce. Vincent this
          is Earl Harold Paul. I've told you
          about him in my letters. You did
          receive my letters.

                    VINCENT ROYCE
          Yes cousin. I trust you've received
          mine? You're in good hands Mr. Earl
          Harold Paul. The SS Ammonothus and
          I will take good care of you, and
          you're lovely wife Maple Mary.

EARL nods his head. DARLENE lets go of embracing him.

                    VINCENT ROYCE (CONT'D)
          Well, good then. Good to see you
          cousin. I'll take your things to
          cabin, Mr. Paul.

EARL nods his head and smiles as Captain ROYCE heads up the
ramp. JAMES gives him a knife and a gun. His employees
stuff his jacket pockets with more knifes and ammo.

                    JAMES TOWNSEND
          If you murder Jeremiah Peterson aboard
          the Ammonothus or anyone else while
          at sea, Vincent will have you thrown
          overboard! When you return we'll
          hunt down his adulterous seed,
          destroying the family of Jeremiah
          Peterson from the face of the earth!

                    EARL HAROLD PAUL
          Gentlemen? Again my many thanks.

DARLENE BAINBRIDGE holds EARL by his arms as he puts his
weapons into his inside jacket pocket and pants pockets.

                    DARLENE BAINBRIDGE
          Remember the sweet power of
          forgiveness. It is stronger and
          mightier than the wicked spirit of
          jealousy and hate.

                    EARL HAROLD PAUL
          I will remember Darlene.

                    DARLENE BAINBRIDGE
          Give your life to jealousy and *She*
          will live on, incubating in your
          heart like a caterpillar in a cocoon,
          nurturing *Her* wretched powers wooing
          your inner mind to madness.

DARLENE wipes her tears away. EARL wipes away her tears and
she just stares at him convinced he won't change.

          DARLENE BAINBRIDGE (CONT'D)
From madness Earl your mind will be
turned into the sickness of self-
destruction and the destruction of
others. My spirit will never leave
your side, my dearest Earl Harold
Paul.

          EARL HAROLD PAUL
You are my friend indeed Darlene
Bainbridge. My sweet, yet, strange
but wonderful friend. I cannot
understand your kindness. Your
goodness to me.

          DARLENE BAINBRIDGE
It is the awesome power of our Lord
inside me that helps me love you.
The chains of despair cannot have my
soul. I by faith declare with all
the power and might of my Matchless
Lord of hope, I will never become a
wicked wretched woman of hate!

          EARL HAROLD PAUL
My life, what would it have become
if only I would have married you
instead?

EARL embraces DARLENE. WAYNE MICKEY MADISON and the US
Marshals dismount.

          DARLENE BAINBRIDGE
Even if you escape this island of
Manhattan aboard the Ammonothus,
they'll kill you if you return.

          WAYNE MICKEY MADISON
Earl? Get on that boat. The city
of Buffalo and the state of New York
forbids you to return...

WAYNE and his Marshals draw their weapons. DARLENE and EARL'S
family and the MADISON family run for cover behind the
carriages as the Marshals open fire.

          WAYNE MICKEY MADISON (CONT'D)
From the dead!

Earl is hit in his right arm and left leg.

          WAYNE MICKEY MADISON (CONT'D)
Cease fire. Cease fire.

                    NANCY VIVIAN VAN HOLT
          You're letting Earl get away?

The friends of Earl helped him on to the cargo vessel. The
ship leaves the Port.

                    WAYNE MICKEY MADISON
          Anna Bella?

A tall curvaceous Italian woman in her 30's with long straight
hair to her waist dressed in a red gown climbs out of the
Marshal's carriage.

                    WAYNE MICKEY MADISON (CONT'D)
          Nancy, that's the last we'll see of
          Mr. Earl Harold Paul. Anna Bella is
          a trained killer. She's a US Marshal.

                    NANCY VIVIAN VAN HOLT
          I've never met her. She must be
          from the island of Manhattan.

She runs to the ramp and gets on to a tug boat that meets
the SS Ammonothus. Nancy is shocked by ANNA BELLA'S
flamboyant style of dress.

                    NANCY VIVIAN VAN HOLT (CONT'D)
          Anna Bella is from this island!

                                        DISSOLVE TO:

25 EXT. DECK OF AMMONOTHUS -- MOMENTS LATER   25

The island of Manhattan is bright with it's city lights while
the moon shines down on the Hudson illuminating her waves
that collide against his majesty's wooden sides. The tug
boat arrives at the side of his majesty. Captain ROYCE
escorts ANNA BELLA on to the deck. EARL is escorted by JAMES,
BOB and TIM. EARL sees that the Professor has the arm of
his wife holding her close to himself. Suppressing his anger,
He walks over to the Professor. Captain Royce quickly takes
the arm of ANNA BELLA and walks up behind EARL.

                    JEREMIAH PETERSON
          Captain? You're not going to leave
          this man aboard this vessel?

                    VINCENT ROYCE
          Well if you don't like any of my
          passengers Professor Jeremiah
          Peterson, get off of my cargo vessel
          right now!

                    JEREMIAH PETERSON
          That won't be necessary. I have too
          much glorious treasure to claim.

                    EARL HAROLD PAUL
          Except this ravishing treasure in
          your arms.

EARL takes the arm of his wife. MAPLE MARY places his arm
around her shoulders.

                    MAPLE MARY
          We have to get these bullets out.
          Lets get inside. I'll tend to your
          wounds. Lets go inside.

                    JEREMIAH PETERSON
          We shall see Earl Harold Paul. We
          shall see.

                    VINCENT ROYCE
          Not on my boat. Not while I'm
          Captain. I'll throw you both over
          to the sharks.

                    ANNA BELLA
          Jeremiah Peterson that is your name.
          My name is Anna Bella from Sicily
          and I love treasure. So tell me
          about your treasure will you?

                    JEREMIAH PETERSON
          Anna Bella! Anna Bella. It would
          be my pleasure to show you my
          treasure! My cabin or yours?

                    ANNA BELLA
          You fool! You're such a *silly* man.
          Yours of course!

ANNA BELLA follows but keeps her eyes on EARL who keeps his
eyes on her. MAPLE MARY stares deep into his eyes. EARL
stops looking at ANNA BELLA when he realizes MAPLE MARY is
looking right at him.

                                        DISSOLVE TO:

26 <u>EXT. SS AMMONOTHUS (MINIATURE)</u> -- DAY   26

The SS Ammonothus is full of the wind with his twenty-one
sails in all of his glory. His majesty is navigated by

Captain Vincent Royce. The Atlantic slams her waves against him as the island of Manhattan sinks into the distant horizon.

DISSOLVE TO:

27 EXT. SS AMMONOTHUS (MINIATURE) -- SUNSET   27

NOVEMBER THANKSGIVING DAY

The Dolphins race him for about five miles before finding their food they require to feast upon. MAPLE MARY finds EARL outside looking at the Dolphins. She gives him a dinner plate of food. EARL lifts his plate to his nose. He frowns. MAPLE MARY laughs. He throws his Thanksgiving dinner into the sea. He grabs his wife and kisses her. She grabs his face and kisses him. Seagulls returning to the Eastern Coast as the SS Ammonothus travel south-east past the equator as more dolphins chase him from behind.

DISSOLVE TO:

28 EXT. SS AMMONOTHUS -- NIGHT   28

DECEMBER 31, 1899

Whales race the great cargo vessel to the Southern tip of Africa. His majesty rests.

From his cabin to the deck of the ship, EARL searches for his wife. ANNA BELLA is dressed in a black gown and diamond jewelry. She follows closely behind EARL for an opportune time to kill him with the knife she conceals in her hands. EARL is walking with a limp and his arm is in a sling. While stumbling through the crowds of people that are drinking and watching the fireworks display, he throws away his bottle of wine over the side. Standing beside Professor JEREMIAH, EARL sees MAPLE MARY. ANNA BELLA sees EARL and follows him through the crowd.

TIM, BOB and JAMES follow ANNA BELLA. VINCENT has another deck that overlooks the entire vessel. From this height he watches through his telescope the New Years party.

More lantern lit tug boats carry additional passengers to the Ammonothus. From on shore fireworks fill the sky in the horizon and above his majesty. The Ammonothus is covered with lantern lights. The city lights of Johannesburg illuminates the horizon on shore while the stars and the full moon illuminates the horizon of the Atlantic.

EARL walks closer to where his wife is standing over looking the ocean, near the bow of the Ammonothus.

EARL walks through the crowd of dancers that are dancing to a waltz performed by an orchestra all celebrating January 1st 1900. The music composition is taken from the published hymn by Composer DARLENE BAINBRIDGE, entitled "Lord of hope".

EARL has his eyes on MAPLE MARY but ANNA BELLA decides to dance with the others in the crowd to the musician's music.

She smiles as she puts the butt of the knife in her mouth. Dancing around the men and women in the crowd she looks dangerously delightful as she bites down hard on the butt of the knife with her teeth.

TIM, BOB and JAMES take out their weapons and point it at ANNA BELLA. The ship's crew apprehends the gentlemen bringing them to the edge of the ship. They are made at gun point to jump on to a tug boat near by. They yell at EARL who can't hear them over the noise of the fireworks display.

EARL massages his wounded arm and walks up behind his wife. JEREMIAH holds MAPLE MARY'S hand but he let's them go when he notices EARL.

EARL firmly lets his hands caress her waist from behind. She turns, a little startled. But she has always desired EARL to approach her that way.

                    MAPLE MARY
          It's been such a long, long, long,
          long, long, long time since you've
          touched me this way. I like it.

Just before EARL kisses MAPLE MARY, he looks at his wife's closed eyes and lips and then stares at JEREMIAH. JEREMIAH is frightened and filled with anger but does not move.

EARL kisses his ravishing MAPLE MARY. She can't believe how good he tastes. She remembers this kind of a kiss. She looks at JEREMIAH. She looks up at EARL and kisses him again and again.

                    EARL HAROLD PAUL
          I'm so thirsty! My lust. My hunger
          for you is my downfall. I get so
          drunk in your love. So intoxicated
          when I am with you Maple Mary.

                    MAPLE MARY
          Drink! Don't talk! Let my kisses
          quench your thirst!

While EARL takes a sip, then a swallow kissing his wife deeply, he notices JEREMIAH is still there. He has not left.

                    MAPLE MARY (CONT'D)
          Will we ever return to Buffalo?

                    EARL HAROLD PAUL
          I don't care. Right now this moment
          with you is all that matters.

                    MAPLE MARY
          We are about to become so rich, we
          will be able to return home bribe a
          few Judges, maybe even President
          William McKinley and everything will
          be wonderful!

Her naivete has never bothered EARL. Only the thought of
another man's desire to have his wife ignites his over
consuming rage. He ignores her ignorance at the impossibility
to return to the life they once knew. He kisses her again.

                    EARL HAROLD PAUL
          Remember this moment! Maple Mary
          don't ever forget this wonderful
          moment in the time of our lives.

                    MAPLE MARY
          Yes. Yes my love this moment is
          wonderful, but the most glorious
          moment is yet to come!

MAPLE'S eyes are still shut. She gently continues to kiss
him. EARL'S eyes water up. His mouth trembles. They kiss
again. Suddenly, he senses the Professor's presence even
though he knew he had never left. While enjoying MAPLE MARY
he opens his eyes and finds the Professor staring with tears
of jealousy.

                    EARL HAROLD PAUL
          What the hell are you looking at?
          Adulterer? You are madly intoxicated
          with Maple Mary. Did you taste her
          sweet tongue?

                    JEREMIAH PETERSON
          Of course, not! No.

                    MAPLE MARY
          Darling? Taste my tongue and quench
          your thirst. Stop taunting Jeremiah!

EARL laughs.

                    EARL HAROLD PAUL
          Taunting him?
                         (MORE)

                    EARL HAROLD PAUL (CONT'D)
          I am going to kill your Professor my
          darling. We are both madly intoxicated
          with my wife. Once you smell the
          scent of another man's wife, you'll
          go mad. The scent of Maple Mary has
          already driven you to madness. So?
          Once more. Kiss my wife! Touch
          her. Now! Like you did in secret.

JEREMIAH steps a few steps closer to kiss her then comes to
his senses. EARL'S eyes are filled with tears. JEREMIAH
takes a step backward astonished at EARL'S words. Then he
moves backward further into the crowd of dancers. MAPLE
MARY continues to enjoy with closed eyes the touch of her
husband.

She opens her eyes and looks at JEREMIAH.

                    EARL HAROLD PAUL (CONT'D)
          Where are you going Professor? You've
          been this close to Maple Mary before!
          So close, you'll never ever forget
          her sweet scent. That is why
          adulterers must die. Their tongues
          are indeed filled with lies.

He starts to go after JEREMIAH. Captain ROYCE aims his pistol
at EARL from his private deck. EARL does not know he is in
danger. The Captain cocks his gun. Allowing himself to be
restrained by MAPLE MARY, they kiss yet again, as if it's
the last moment they'll ever share together. VINCENT ROYCE
withdraws his gun.

JEREMIAH leaves backing away into the arms of ANNA BELLA who
is five inches taller than he is. Dancing around him, she
takes her knife out of her mouth and stuffs it in his safari
outfit front pocket. She lifts her arms slowly over her
head towards the night sky. JEREMIAH buries his nose between
her breasts and holds her waist tightly to himself. He looks
up. Looking into his eyes she smiles.

                    ANNA BELLA
          Never forget my scent, no never forget
          my scent. Never forget my scent, no
          never ever forget my sweet scent!

She repeats these words over and over again as they dance in
the center of the crowded deck.

                                        DISSOLVE TO:

29 **EXT. SS AMMONOTHUS (MINIATURE)-- EVENING**   29

His majesty leaves with the winds and strong currents of the
Southern Atlantic Ocean around the African tip through the
Indian Sea to Cairo's Harbor Port Authority. His majesty
rests in the land of Egypt. The sounds of marine merchant
workers unloading the sail vessel fill the air. An Arabic
melody sung by an Egyptian worker is carried by the wind.

                                              FADE OUT:

FADE IN:

30 **INT. EARL & MAPLE MARY'S CABIN SUITE -- MORNING**   30

Occasionally there's a shout or two in Arabic as workers
continue to fill the air with noise of the laborious task of
unloading the SS Ammonothus. EARL'S cabin window is open.
He lay in bed startled by the shouting. He turns and tries
to fall asleep. A crate falls on the deck awaking EARL to
find he is alone in his room. He gets dressed in a hurry
and takes his gun and a knife placing them in his shoulder
bag. He looks out of the window.

31 **EXT. EARL'S CABIN WINDOW & DOCKING BAY** -- CONTINUOUS   31

EARL sees Captain ROYCE standing on the dock looking up at
him. He hears the singing of Muslim worshipers come to a
stop as those Egyptian workers resume their daily task along
side of East African and Chinese workers. Tied to the sail
post is ANNA BELLA, TIM, BOB and JAMES. Two guards are
pointing rifles at their heads. Their heads are covered by
empty sand bags.

                    VINCENT ROYCE
          Morning! Tea?

                    EARL HAROLD PAUL
          No. You know what I want!

                    VINCENT ROYCE
          Can't it wait 'til afternoon?

                    EARL HAROLD PAUL
          Why waste this morning?

                    VINCENT ROYCE
          Well...let's see, you need a lift
          won't you now?

                    EARL HAROLD PAUL
          Yes right away. Why?

Vincent revealed who was under the sand bags by lifting the
bags off of their heads one at a time.

> VINCENT ROYCE
> I'm tied up at the moment or should
> I say-lovely Ms. Anna Bella here
> wants to kill you. And on New Years
> morning when you were kissing your
> pretty wife Maple Mary I
> caught...you'll never guess Bob, Tim
> and my cousin James trying to kill
> Anna Bella who was trying to kill
> you aboard my ship. Turns out she's
> a US Marshal. Well, you know my
> rule.

> EARL HAROLD PAUL
> You're not going to shoot your cousin
> James? He's a friend of mine and
> Bob and Tim. They're all friends of
> mine...even the lovely US Marshal
> Ms. Anna Bella who wants to kill me.

> VINCENT ROYCE
> Because they're friends of yours,
> and because one of them is my cousin
> who daringly boarded my ship when in
> South Africa I left him and his
> comrades on a tug boat...I'll tell
> you what I'll do. I'll leave your
> friends right here until we both
> return. That will be their punishment
> for breaking my rules about attempted
> murder aboard my vessel.

> EARL HAROLD PAUL
> Fine. I'll be right out.

> VINCENT ROYCE
> I'll get my carriage ready.

> EARL HAROLD PAUL
> Oh and friends, please thank the
> Captain for his mercy upon your wicked
> wretched lives!

> FRIENDS OF EARL
> Thank you Captain!

Vincent places the sand bags over their heads while the guards
who are the members of his crew aim rifles at their heads.

DISSOLVE TO:

32 <u>EXT. VINCENT ROYCE'S CARRIAGE</u> -- MOMENTS LATER   32

VINCENT hands EARL his gun. EARL refuses and shows him the
weapons he already has. EARL has tears in his eyes and a
serious stern look then suddenly he laughs. He repeats this
behavior continually. Because of the stench of his sins,
one of his *tears* takes flight defying gravity for the first
time. VINCENT and EARL notice this strange phenomenon.

                                           DISSOLVE TO:

33 <u>EXT. AMMONOTHUS ANCIENT TRANSPORT TOMB SITE</u> -- DAY   33

Egyptian guards are posted with rifles. Signs are on wooden
posts written in English and Arabic: *Ammonothus Ancient
Transport Tomb Site Stay Out! Private Exhibition of Professor
Jeremiah Peterson.*

A picture of himself dressed in a safari outfit is posted
next to the sign.

The guards point their rifles at EARL. He stares them down.
In fear, they lower their rifles as he passes them by.

                    VINCENT ROYCE
          I'll be right here! Enjoy the hunt!

Holding his knife EARL lifts his hand in the air and waves.

34 <u>INT. TRANSPORT MACHINE POD CHAMBER</u> -- MOMENTS LATER   34

MAPLE MARY straddles Professor PETERSON'S lap as he sits in
the transport machine. Drops of sweat run down his face as
MAPLE MARY licks his sweat while giving him the kisses he
has always secretly enjoyed from her. He finds his knife in
his front safari pocket and takes it out. She removes the
knife from her black girder belt. It's the knife her aunt
Charlotte Ann gave her.

35 <u>INT. TRANSPORT MACHINE POD</u> -- CONTINUOUS   35

Professor PETERSON kisses MAPLE MARY who returns his
affections. She caresses his face and neck with both knives.
He finally closes his eyes. Suddenly, he is startled,
saddened and surprised all at the same time as he feels her
press both knives deeper into his chest.

She twists both knives into his chest as she continues to
kiss him her wet sweet kisses.

JEREMIAH begins to weep.

MAPLE MARY kisses his tears and saliva filled mouth.

                    MAPLE MARY
          Did you think I'd leave my husband
          for you Professor Jeremiah Peterson?

                    JEREMIAH PETERSON
          But! You did leave him for me my
          darling Maple Mary. Yes! Yes you
          did leave your husband for me.

                    MAPLE MARY
          No my sweet dearest Jeremiah!

MAPLE MARY watches as he faints in his chair. EARL comes up
from behind her. He touches the small part of her back with
his fingers. She is startled a little but then she begins
to kiss her husband. She hands him both knives.

                    EARL HAROLD PAUL
          Darling I have my own. Now make
          love to me the way you did last night.

They toss JEREMIAH on to the floor. EARL sits in the chair
while MAPLE MARY straps him in. She takes off her blouse.
Her curves are too much for EARL to take so he begins licking
her cleavage as she unsnaps her bra. He kisses her ravishing
her charms. Her orgasms fulfill her completely.

She has not been touched by him like this in such a long
long long long time.

                    MAPLE MARY
          Earl my darling we will be rich just
          like my parents and all my friends
          on the island of Manhattan!

With one hand EARL places the sharp edge of both knives
against her neck. MAPLE MARY begins to bleed.

                    EARL HAROLD PAUL
          Shut your pretty mouth! Drink! One
          last time let me quench your thirst.
          You felt the Professor inside of
          you?

                    MAPLE MARY
          Yes! But with Jeremiah's discovery
          of the Ammonothus Tomb and this
          ancient carriage you will find great
          fortune for us! Jeremiah was inside
          me but it only meant you could become
          rich!

MAPLE MARY turns on the machine pulling a lever. EARL
suddenly believes the cave is spinning in circles as the

machine is causing them both to be pulled into the 4th
dimension.

The transport pod begins to travel down a fourth dimensional
plane as it moves down a tunnel. EARL kisses MAPLE MARY.
MAPLE MARY kisses EARL with tears in her eyes. She kisses
and tastes the tears that run down his face.

His tears begin to defy gravity as they rest at the top of
the worm hole tunnel of the 4th dimension.

                    EARL HAROLD PAUL
          My love for you Maple Mary has always
          been rich!

                    MAPLE MARY
          Even with all of your employees
          cleaning the cobblestone streets of
          Buffalo and Niagara Falls Park,
          compared to my family you were so
          damned poor Earl Harold Paul. What
          was a girl like I suppose to do?
          Earl? What was I suppose to do?

                    EARL HAROLD PAUL
          Love and honor me my sweet Maple
          Mary. You were suppose to always
          love and honor me!

Earl Harold Paul slashes, with one stroke, the throat of his
beloved MAPLE MARY. EARL weeps. While he ravishes her
breasts and charms, he feels her warm blood run down his
face.

His tears escapes his eye lids as if they were filled with
helium. His tears take flight with the wind and ascend into
the air above him.

The ancient Egyptian tunnel which were made by the Nephilim
centuries ago comes to an end.

But the transport pod machine vanishes through the wall of
sulfur stones and comes to a stop at the Temple Tomb of
Ammonothus after smashing through several iceberg columns
that hold up the underground cavern structure beneath the
surface of Antarctica.

36 <u>INT. AMMONOTHUS ANCIENT TRANSPORT TOMB</u>-- CONTINUOUS   36

Earl Harold Paul shivers from the cold of the underground
cavern and the Temple Tomb's corridors. At the alter he
sees the sixteen-foot hybrid Nephilim, AMMONOTHUS.

He is clothed like a warrior with a sword, helmet, shield
and cape. Underground vents of fire and smoke warm the Temple
near the alter. These vents extend into the bottom of the
ocean floor where heat escapes from the earth's core.

                    AMMONOTHUS
          I lived here beneath this Antarctic
          ice for centuries ever since the
          Judge of Light, the creator of all
          the living sentenced my father
          Ammontai who was a Watcher, an angelic
          warrior of the sky, to a place called
          Tartarus. It is the Hell of Hells.
          A place reserved for angels like my
          father who slept with human women.
          I've been here for centuries waiting
          for you to come to me.

                    EARL HAROLD PAUL
          What is you name?

                    AMMONOTHUS
          I am called Ammonothus.

                    EARL HAROLD PAUL
          I am called Earl Harold Paul.

                    AMMONOTHUS
          What a joy it is to see face to face
          the one whom I will give my wretched
          glory. You will become my first
          immortal man.

EARL watches as half of the Temple and the Cavern of ice and
stone becomes a 4th dimensional window into the past life of
AMMONOTHUS. EARL for a moment forgets about his wife. He
leaves her in a pool of her own blood in the transport pod
and walks through the cavern near the alter with AMMONOTHUS
THE WRAITH MAN.

He shows EARL his angelic father in a courtroom sitting in
the witness chair. The room is filled with angels and a
ghostly being who is called the JUDGE of LIGHT. The JUDGE
of LIGHT is seated in his chair.

                    AMMONOTHUS (V.O.) (CONT'D)
          I hate the Creator. I hate the Judge
          of Light for what he did to my Father.
          My father Ammontai was only guilty
          of love. He loved Haggai my mother.
          She was a wonderful and beautiful
          North African woman.
                         (MORE)

> AMMONOTHUS (V.O.) (CONT'D)
> When the Judge of Light sentenced my
> father to Tartarus, it destroyed my
> mother's will to live.

HAGGAI pleads with him to kill her at the alter of the tomb.
EARL watches the fourth dimensional vision. He witnesses
the moment that AMMONOTHUS draws his sword. EARL is horrified
as he sees HAGGAI continually being assaulted by her son.

AMMONOTHUS begins to cut his arm with his sword he used to
kill her. He begins to cut his arm with his sword as his
mother bleeds to death. AMMONOTHUS takes his dagger and
cuts his own throat.

He falls and bleeds to death beside his mother.

> AMMONOTHUS (V.O.) (CONT'D)
> I took the life of my mother so that
> she may become a martyr for my father.
> Then. I took my own life.

EARL sees the transformation of AMMONOTHUS. Gazing into the
fourth dimensional vision, EARL sees the spirit of AMMONOTHUS
become hideous to look upon.

> AMMONOTHUS (V.O.) (CONT'D)
> On that day I became a Wraith, a
> wicked wretched horrid spirit.

For a moment EARL stops looking into the fourth dimensional
window and begins to step closer to AMMONOTHUS who is standing
near the underground vent. EARL realizes the closer he walks
towards AMMONOTHUS he becomes warmer. He notices that his
wounds are completely healed. He removes the sling from his
arm.

EARL'S face shines with perspiration. He goes back to the
transport pod and picks up MAPLE MARY in his arms. Listening
to AMMONOTHUS THE WRAITH MAN, he kisses his wife's lips.

MAPLE MARY refuses to loose consciousness.

> AMMONOTHUS (CONT'D)
> Cast your wife into this underground
> vent of fire and smoke. I will take
> her spirit and imprison her here in
> the walls of my temple for all
> eternity.

EARL casts his wife into the flames while his tears defy
gravity. His tears float away evaporating above his head.

AMMONOTHUS (CONT'D)
Now kneel before me Earl Harold Paul
and I will give you immortality.
You will become as I am now. Kneel
my wretched human servant.

Then the 4th dimensional window into AMMONOTHUS'S past life
gradually disappears.

AMMONOTHUS (CONT'D)
I anoint you with my darkened eternal
light. Feel the absence of peace I
feel. With your free will, let the
spirit of our minds become one.

EARL HAROLD PAUL
What do you want of me, Ammonothus?

AMMONOTHUS
Allow me to kill all you wish to
kill through the passing of eternal
time. Until you take your own life,
I will be your Master giving to you
life that can never be ended except
by your own hands!

EARL HAROLD PAUL
I wish to take the lives of all those
descendants of Professor Jeremiah
Peterson. To take the lives of those
wanton men who destroy the bond of
matrimony and the gift of love I and
my Maple Mary once shared.

AMMONOTHUS
Your will be accomplished. Oh, what
a horrid time we will have together
Earl Harold Paul. As the Wraith
Man, I will not act on my own but
only through you. Through you, my
satisfaction of exterminating the
Judge of Light's gift of life to man
will be complete. Through me, your
thirst for vengeance will be quenched.

EARL HAROLD PAUL
We are of one mind Ammonothus. My
life is yours. My Wraith Master.

AMMONOTHUS
Your faith in me has allowed you to
become as I am. Now, we are both
Wicked Wretched Wraith Men.

As EARL and AMMONOTHUS face one another, a ray of energy is passed on to EARL. He takes off his sling. He is completely healed. Together they stretch forth their hands toward MAPLE MARY'S body. Energy flows out of their hands. They lift MAPLE MARY'S spirit out of her body. EARL and the WRAITH MAN keep her spirit suspended in the air as they imprison her in one of the pillar columns of the Temple.

>   EARL HAROLD PAUL
>   Maple Mary? You've got what you've
>   always wanted. You're imprisoned in
>   this Temple Tomb, in this magnificent
>   archeological find. This place may
>   yet become the next Wonder of the
>   World!

MAPLE MARY screams in anger but there is no sound that comes out of her voice while trying to free herself, as the energy of immortality that illuminates and radiates from EARL and AMMONOTHUS grows brighter filling the entire Temple Tomb.

>   EARL HAROLD PAUL (CONT'D)
>   You look so horrid! Frightened?
>   Why? You're rich beyond your wildest
>   dreams, far wealthier than all your
>   friends and family. Someday I'll be
>   imprisoned there beside you, after
>   many years, perhaps centuries of
>   cutting down the family trees of the
>   Jeremiah Petersons of the world.

Glowing energy from AMMONOTHUS whirls around EARL like a tornado towering thirty-five feet.

This world wind of energy reaches to the top of the Temple Tomb's mosaic decorated ceiling of stone and statues of Nephilim Warriors with their deformed mouths wide open.

>   EARL HAROLD PAUL (CONT'D)
>   Now, you understand that the sweet
>   wine of your love was meant for only
>   me. My sweet darling, Maple Mary,
>   don't worry. After I take my own
>   life, our beloved Nephilim Master
>   will bring my spirit here to be with
>   you, for all time!

                                        FADE OUT:

Buffalo NEWSPAPER CLIPPINGS Headliner Sequence:

37 *RAYMOND HARRISON'S MAIN TITLE SCORE PERFORMED --*   37
CONTINUOUS

FADE IN:

                                        DISSOLVE TO:

APPLEGATE SUNDAY TIMES October 28,1900

Maimed Murdered Men are Silenced! Found Tongueless! Strange
Clue? Bottles of Goats Milk Filled with German Wolf Shepherd
Hairs!

                                        DISSOLVE TO:

NIAGARA FALLS NORTHERN STAR January 28,1909

Adulterers Beware! Stay far away from Buffalo! Wanton Men
Visit Niagara Falls Park At Your Own Peril!

                                        DISSOLVE TO:

THE BUFFALO CANADIAN CHRONICLE July 28,1929

Ammonothus Sightings! Overpopulated Water and Gardens
Sanitarium Builds new Ward Annex.

                                        DISSOLVE TO:

THE BUFFALO NEW YORK COMET April 28,1939

Beheaded Man Found in Niagara Falls Park-his wife accused of
murder of passion! Woman gives birth to Earl Harold Paul's
Son! Acquitted! Lack of Evidence!

                                        DISSOLVE TO:

APPLEGATE TELEVISION HERALD October 28,1949

More Pregnant Women Claim Earl Harold Paul Murdered their
cheating husbands and fathered their children! Court Grants
Custody to Mr. Paul. His Estate a Grand Nursery?

                                        DISSOLVE TO:

NIAGARA FALLS NORTHERN STAR January 28,1959

Earl Harold Paul Waste Management Systems Controls City's
Sewage. Employees of Earl Keep Niagara Falls Park Immaculate!
Buffalo, New York has never been cleaner!

                                        DISSOLVE TO:

APPLEGATE NIAGARA GLOBE April 28,1969

Happy Birthday Earl! How old are you? Quote: "I'm America's First Immortal Man!?"

DISSOLVE TO:

THE BUFFALO CANADIAN CHRONICLE July 28,1979

Mr. Earl Harold Paul! Wicked? Wretched? Or a Waste Management System Genius! All of the Above?

DISSOLVE TO:

APPLEGATE NIAGARA GLOBE October 28,1989

One hundred floating heads found falling in the raging river of Niagara. Witnesses Claim they fell from the midnight sky out of the arms of Ammonothus the Wraith Man!?

DISSOLVE TO:

APPLEGATE TELEVISION HERALD January 28,1999

Twelve Maimed Tongueless Men Confess their sins at Buffalo Methodist Cathedral of Mercy, afterwards committed suicide by jumping off the Bell Tower of the church. A note was found. "Who can save us from Ammonothus the Wraith Man!?" Buffalo, New York 1999;

DISSOLVE TO:

APPLEGATE SUNDAY TIMES April 28,2000

HAPPY 2000! BUFFALO.
HUNDREDS GREET THE NEW CENTURY GAZING UP AT THE BELL TOWER OF **BUFFALO METHODIST CATHEDRAL OF MERCY. MANY CLAIM** TO HAVE SEEN THE **SPIRIT** OF **DARLENE BAINBRIDGE** HOVERING ABOVE THE CHURCH; PUBLISHED HYMN **COMPOSER, DAUGHTER OF THE PARISH FOUNDERS** WHO DIED IN 1899.
HER PARENTS WERE **MURDERED** BY EARL HAROLD PAUL!?

DISSOLVE TO:

FULL SHOT OF TEXT: PRESENT DAY

DISSOLVE TO:

38 EXT. "NEW" DODGE SILVER RAM HEMI TRUCK -- MORNING   38

DAVEY SANDS drives his boss EMMA PETERSON to EHP Waste Management Systems Plant. Bags and boxes of trash from *Emma's Tailor & Bizarre Costume Shop* fill the back of the vehicle. EMMA is a married 34 year old slender brunette with voluptuous charms. She has three children who are in their preteens.

DAVEY SANDS is a dark skinned fellow age 21 who is a native
of Jamaica with dreadlocks that extend passed his steroid
built shoulders.

                    DAVEY SANDS
          Why am I driving this trash to the
          EHP Waste Plant, Mrs. Peterson?

                    EMMA PETERSON
          You forgot as always to do your job.
          Why am I explaining something that I
          assign you every week?

                    DAVEY SANDS
          I just don't want to be seen by Earl
          Harold Paul or any of his employees
          that are his sons or relatives, which
          is practically the whole Plant!

                    EMMA PETERSON
          Pay attention! Turn into the drive
          way.

DAVEY drives on to the Plant's property while a lovely Puerto
Rican woman guard named GLORIA walks over to the truck. He
starts to chew on his own hair. He does this constantly
when he is nervous. EMMA takes his hair out of his mouth.
Davey puts his hair back into his mouth.

MR. PAUL'S black Hummer limo exits the plant then stops beside
EMMA'S Ram halfback that has her company's logo on both sides
of the cab's doors.

39 EXT. EHP WASTE MANAGEMENT SYSTEMS PLANT FRONT GATE --   39
CONTINUOUS

EARL presses his window down and sees EMMA exiting the car
and walk up to his window. The guard prevents EMMA getting
near the Hummer Limo. EARL HAROLD PAUL looks as if he has
not aged. He still looks 45 years old as he did in 1899.

                    GLORIA THE GUARD
          Ms.? Can I be of any assistance?

                    EARL HAROLD PAUL
          You must be one of my new employees!

                    GLORIA THE GUARD
          Yes sir Mr. Paul. Well, I started a
          mouth ago.

                    EARL HAROLD PAUL
          Have some of my boys take care of...

                   GLORIA THE GUARD
        I'll call Mr. Luther the foreman.

                   EARL HAROLD PAUL
        You do that-call Luther...that will
        be all.

GLORIA starts to speak but returns to her post.

                   EMMA PETERSON
        I'm Emma Peterson! My employee forgot
        to empty the trash. He didn't do
        his chore, he's a good worker but
        sometimes...well...So I made him
        drive all the way here. I hope it's
        not too much trouble to take my...

                   EARL HAROLD PAUL
        You're Mrs. Emma Peterson? Your
        husband is a lawyer?

EMMA nods her head.

                   EMMA PETERSON
        I admire a man who, with just one
        look, can read everything there is
        about me just by looking into my
        eyes. I wish I could be psychic
        like that. I just don't have the
        gift.

EARL points his finger at GLORIA still on the phone at her
post.

                   EARL HAROLD PAUL
        Her trash! Her garbage! Get rid of
        it now!

                   GLORIA THE GUARD
        What? I am on the phone with Luther.
        Ok. Sir, Mr. Paul! Luther get your
        lazy ass down here now. Mr. Paul
        just yelled at me. I don't know why
        he's yelling at me.

                   EMMA PETERSON
        I'm not as talented as you. Will
        you teach me? Murder my husband.
        Would you do that? Could you do
        that? He has a dirty rotten tongue
        that is always filled with lies.

The Plant's sliding gates open. LUTHER a five tall Irish
man in his 60's waves DAVEY forward.

DAVEY hesitates but presses his foot on the exhaust. The
truck is still in "park".

EMMA stares at DAVEY. She can't help it, EMMA is embarrassed
so she yells.

> EMMA PETERSON (CONT'D)
> Davey? Drive on to the Plant!

Instantly she calms down as she gazes into EARL'S eyes.

She turns to DAVEY whose hands are shaking. He mumbles
something that can't be understood. He tries to psyche
himself into pressing the gas pedal. He looks at his EMMA.

> EMMA PETERSON (CONT'D)
> Don't embarrass me in front of this
> handsome tabloid man.

> DAVEY SANDS
> You're going to really make me do
> this Mrs. Peterson?

Tears start to flow from his eyes. He is frightened.

> DAVEY SANDS (CONT'D)
> I am quitting after today!

Extremely bothered by DAVEY'S timidness, she tries to hold
her anger in *"check"*.

> EMMA PETERSON
> That will be good then. You do that.

EMMA looks down into EARL'S eyes. He looks into hers. He
smiles. She smiles.

> EMMA PETERSON (CONT'D)
> Sorry.

DAVEY SANDS drives on to the plant past the guard shack. A
trash vehicle stops by EMMA'S Hemi Ram pickup. Men exit the
EHP Vehicle and remove the trash from EMMA'S company vehicle.

> EMMA PETERSON (CONT'D)
> Mr. Paul I presume, you are Earl
> Harold Paul?

> EARL HAROLD PAUL
> Yes. I am Earl Harold Paul. Dine
> with me at Niagara Falls Seafood
> Palace.

> EMMA PETERSON
> I own a shop. Here's my card. Stop
> in sometime if you need a costume or
> if you need some tailoring done. I
> sew! Professionally! All the time,
> five days a week.

> EARL HAROLD PAUL
> Thank you. Mrs. Peterson! I'll
> stop by tomorrow after I have
> breakfast with the children. Here's
> my card.

She takes it. She hears what he just said after. Reading
his name.

> EMMA PETERSON
> Call me Emma! Oh you're married.
> Oh, no!

EARL presses the window up. He looks forward as if he's
uninterested.

The limo drives away as EARL glances through the back glass
at EMMA who stares at the limo driving away.

> EMMA PETERSON (CONT'D)
> Divorce her ass. I'm divorcing mine.

DAVEY SANDS drives out the exit ramp. EMMA enters the vehicle
and looks through her purse.

> EMMA PETERSON (CONT'D)
> You can leave right now Mr. Sands.
> Walk home. Your check will be in
> the mail.

She mumbles to herself.

> EMMA PETERSON (CONT'D)
> I have my license? Yes! I love you
> Emma. Didn't forget it this time.

She looks at the tearful DAVEY SANDS in pity.

> EMMA PETERSON (CONT'D)
> Get your ass out of my company
> vehicle. You must be cheating on
> your wife.

She smiles.

>   EMMA PETERSON (CONT'D)
>   That's why. Don't be afraid of Earl
>   Harold Paul or any of his clean up
>   crew that drive through this town.
>   Adulterer. I'll cut your dirty rotten
>   tongue myself if you don't get your
>   stinkin' ass out of my truck.

EMMA gets out of the passenger side and walks over to the
driver's side.

>   DAVEY SANDS
>   I'm, I'm sorry, so sorry I'll drive
>   you anywhere, any place your heart
>   desires Mrs. Peterson. The freak
>   saw me. Let's just get away from
>   here! I'm cheating on my wife, Ok?

>   EMMA PETERSON
>   Freak? Earl Harold Paul is one fine
>   freak of a man. Honey! Look at me.
>   I knew you were screwing around...You
>   and my soon to be ex-husband are
>   both the same. All of you dirty
>   rotten dogs love to screw!

DAVEY SANDS looks at EMMA. EMMA stares back at him as a
trash truck drives on to the property. The operator stops
the truck. DAVEY looks over EMMA'S shoulder at the driver.

>   EMMA PETERSON (CONT'D)
>   Don't worry about Mr. Paul or
>   Ammonothus the Wraith Man. I'll
>   take that rotten life you're living
>   away from you...for all the lies
>   you've told your precious sweet Hanna.

DAVEY'S eyes begin to water.

>   EMMA PETERSON (CONT'D)
>   ...Mr. Sands? Get out of my vehicle!
>   See you tomorrow.

>   DAVEY SANDS
>   How did you know I was having an
>   affair with a married woman?

>   EMMA PETERSON
>   Goodbye Davey!

The truck operator presses the gas of his garbage truck engine
while taking out a knife and pretending to cut his own throat.

He then points his blade in DAVEY'S direction then withdraws his weapon out of sight just as EMMA turns to see what DAVEY is excited about. EMMA smiles at the operator who returns her smile. EMMA turns and looks at DAVEY. There's no way she is going to allow him to drive her anywhere, not anymore today or any time soon.

She opens the door of her truck.

> EMMA PETERSON (CONT'D)
> I am not going to fire your pathetic ass.

DAVEY gets out of the vehicle. She pushes him aside and enters her pickup. DAVEY moves back in the way of the driver's door. EMMA tries to close the door.

> EMMA PETERSON (CONT'D)
> Get out! Mr. Sands? Go wherever you go when you don't go home...Get some rest? Screw!

Gloria the guard approaches the driver side of the garbage truck and notices the employee badge of the driver. She waves her hand for him to proceed then walks back to her post at the guard shack. The EHP garbage truck enters the facility.

EMMA leaves the door open and drives off. Her door closes due to the motion of the vehicle. She opens and shuts the door and secures it properly.

DAVEY runs after EMMA'S Hemi Ram pickup.

40 EXT. "NEW" DODGE SILVER RAM HEMI TRUCK -- MOMENTS LATER
40

EMMA sees a block and a half down the street a senior citizen with a big octagon stop sign in her hand and school kids at the corner waiting for the light to change. EMMA looks in her rear view mirror.

DAVEY SANDS is about to jump inside of her truck. EMMA looks forward. The light is still green. She presses on the exhaust pedal.

> EMMA PETERSON
> Not today Davey! Not ever again.

EMMA keeps her eye on the green light hoping it will not change.

Suddenly, parked cars are thrown off to the side smashing into the windows of store fronts by an invisible force.

DAVEY looks over his shoulder and runs faster as the cars
being tossed are getting closer to him, as if someone knocking
cars out of the way is running behind, trying to catch up.

She sees the light change to red. EMMA stops the vehicle
and smiles at the children as they cross the street with the
65 year old woman school crossing guard leading the way.

The children notice the cars being tossed to the side of the
sidewalk and get back on to the curb. Some kids point.

> SCHOOL CHILDREN
> Ammonothus the Wraith Man! He's
> coming, he's coming here he comes!

EMMA smiles, motioning them to cross. She has the window
rolled up so she did not hear what they had just said. The
school children motion her to drive off.

The parked cars are being violently thrown on the side walk
and into the store-fronts coming closer to the corner. The
school crossing guard runs to the other side of the street
without the children who are too scared to move.

> EMMA PETERSON
> I'm going to report your ass you
> just wait!

The light changes green.

Just as she presses her foot on the exhaust pedal DAVEY
reaches the truck and jumps inside. He lays down shivering
all over.

Two vehicles turning on to the street behind EMMA'S vehicle
are thrown into each other. EMMA looks in her rear view
mirror and comes to a complete stop. She doesn't know DAVEY
is laying down inside.

Believing she has just missed an accident, she's about to
open the door when she spots the woman school crossing guard
run across the street to get the children she had left behind.
She notices the children running, leaving the crossing guard
behind them as they make it safely to the other side of the
corner.

> EMMA PETERSON (CONT'D)
> Kids are ok. Good! Morning drivers
> and incompetent school crossing
> guards.

EMMA drives off.

FADE OUT:

FADE IN:

41 <u>EXT. JACOB PETERSON BUILDING</u> -- MOMENTS LATER   41

EMMA drives her truck into the parking lot. She gets out and enters the law firm not realizing DAVEY is still in the back of her vehicle. He was murdered by AMMONOTHUS. Cop cars following in pursuit surround the parking lot. They find DAVE'S body. The officers enter the law firm.

DISSOLVE TO:

42 <u>EXT. JACOB PETERSON BUILDING</u> -- CONTINUOUS   42

Applegate News Crew driving their Chevy Suburbans and broadcast Vans drive on to the Law Firm parking lot.

DISSOLVE TO:

43 <u>P.O.V. APPLEGATE NEWS HELICOPTER</u> -- MOMENTS LATER   43

As her helicopter news crew hovers over the Jacob Peterson Law Firm and streets surrounding the Firm's property, Reporter Agnes Anna Applegate talks to her Television audience. She is an African-American woman in her 50's from a long line of news journalists. Her family owns a television station and three local news papers in downtown Buffalo.

> AGNES ANNA APPLEGATE (V.O.)
> Someday I and my family of news
> journalists will be believed. My
> job here at Applegate Television
> Studios is to simply open the eyes
> of those who have doubted our
> credibility in the past. Since the
> early 1900's my family has brought
> you the news of local and national
> events including the strange
> phenomenon known as Ammonothus the
> Wraith Man! I firmly believe that
> he is the demonic presence who is
> connected somehow with
> multimillionaire Earl Harold Paul.
> He founded EHP Waste Management
> Systems Plant! Mr. Paul is more
> than a man ladies and gentlemen. He
> is an immortal man.

The sound of a knife striking something is heard repeatedly.

44 <u>EXT. APPLEGATE NEWS HELICOPTER</u> -- CONTINUOUS   44

> AGNES ANNA APPLEGATE
> Let's climb higher! Captain Howard?

CAPTAIN HOWARD
Yes Agnes Anna Applegate. Hovering
Higher as you wish.

45 <u>P.O.V. **APPLEGATE NEWS HELICOPTER**</u> -- CONTINUOUS   45

AGNES ANNA APPLEGATE
Thank you Captain Howard. And as
you can see, the destruction of cars
thrown to the side of the buildings.
It's the work of Ammonothus the Wraith
Man!

46 <u>INT. **EARL'S ESTATE GRAND LIVING ROOM**</u> -- CONTINUOUS   46

EARL sits in his chase lounge. His great room is decorated
in black, gold and white colors. Sitting in his leather
sectional sofa that surrounds a fifty inch plasma screen.

He beats himself on his legs with his knife while mumbling
his death song. On the wall above the large fireplace an
original portrait of MAPLE MARY is displayed. EARL kept the
family portrait of her family. The hand painted portrait
hangs beside hers. Newer digital pictures of Earl with
different women and the children he has fathered over the
decades are in picture frames resting on the mantel. A
picture of his Butler Charles Gibbons and his adopted son
NATHAN is among the pictures. A current picture of BOB, TIM
and JAMES standing on a yacht beside EARL is among the
collection of pictures. Like EARL, his Butler CHARLES, and
friends BOB, TIM and JAMES have not aged.

EARL is dressed in his bathrobe and pajamas and slippers
from Brooks Brothers. His initials EHP are stitched on his
clothes.

AGNES ANNA APPLEGATE
For Applegate News here in Buffalo,
this is Agnes Anna Applegate reporting
to you live from high above the Law
Firm of Jacob Peterson.

EARL smiles. He nods his head. He begins to mumble his
death song in a whisper as he listens to Reporter APPLEGATE.

As he watches her newscast he raises his voice as he chants
repeatedly.

More news footage; footage of cars being thrown to the side
of the street as men are being chased by an invisible force,
with the heading on the newscast "Ammonothus sightings caught
on Video."

EARL is joined by members of his family who chant along with him repeatedly as they all watch the APPLEGATE NEWS broadcast.

They are all dressed in their custom embroidered bathrobes, pajamas and slippers.

APPLEGATE NEWS footage of the *Ammonothus Sightings* ends and the broadcast picture returns as police vehicles surround the Jacob Peterson Building.

EARL and his family begin to whisper the death song as the double doors of the dining room are opened by CHARLES while AMMONOTHUS is seated at the head of the table.

                    EARL & FAMILY
      Adulterers. You'll die die die!
      Your dirty rotten tongues are filled
      with lies! Cut cut cut I'll cut
      your tongues, so you won't taste
      taste taste the sweet ravishing flavor
      of other men's wives!

Although He is invisible the robe he's wearing is seen. Clothed like a Jesuit Priest, he does not show his fleshly form yet. His only jewelry is a golden chain and medallion with a sulfur stone in the middle. There are no religious symbols he wears. A golden picture frame is on the wall behind him. It is a hand brushed painting of EARL SR.

                    AMMONOTHUS
      Breakfast is served! Let us have
      our morning feast.

                    CHARLES GIBBONS
      You may be the resident Wraith of
      this Mansion, and I am not ungrateful
      for the immortality you've given me
      again...So!

CHARLES begins to sing the family to the table.

The children are overjoyed and join in the Charles Gibbon*s Tune.* They number 6 boys and 7 girls. The other guests are Bob, Tim, and James and their wives.

                  CHARLES GIBBONS (CONT'D)
      Chop chop chop! Let's go, to the
      table lets go...Come one come all
      and please if you would...take, your,
      seats!

                   CHILDREN OF EARL
      One more time! Take your seats!
          (MORE)

                    CHILDREN OF EARL (CONT'D)
One more time! Take your seats!
One more time! Take your seats!
One more time...

                    AMMONOTHUS
Silence!

                    CHARLES GIBBONS
Stand by the door. Stand by the
door! Hold hands and wait until I
escort you in. Innocent ears are
covered!

The CHILDREN OF EARL reluctantly obey and cover their ears.
They stand on the outside of the double doors to the dining
room.

47 INT. EARL'S ESTATE GRAND DINING ROOM -- MORNING   47

As the household enters the grand dining room, they continue
to whisper the chant. EARL is seated at the other end.
Behind him is the picture of his mother. He stops chanting.
He bows his head and closes his eyes. The other seats of
his family members are held by his staff of servers and cooks.

Each family member stops chanting when they are seated.
They take their seat one at a time counter clock wise.

The dining room is silent.

EARL raises his voice speaking his prayer aloud. The rest
of the household, including the servants, repeats his prayer
in a whisper.

                    EARL HAROLD PAUL
          A moment of silence is given by this
          family for the memory of my beloved
          wife Maple Mary.

                    EVERYONE EXCEPT EARL
          A moment of silence is given by this
          family for the memory of Maple Mary.

EARL lifts his head and opens his eyes as tears flow upward
towards the ceiling.

                    EARL HAROLD PAUL
          Hallelujah!

                    EVERYONE
          Hallelujah!

                    EARL HAROLD PAUL
    Amen!

                      EVERYONE
    Amen!

As EARL lowers his head, the cooks pour his hot oatmeal and
raisins into his cereal bowl that has the image of MAPLE
MARY designed into the center. His eyes dry within seconds.

The other family members raise their heads, open their eyes
and wait to be served. Every bowl has the image of MAPLE
MARY designed onto them.

Wraith Master AMMONOTHUS, clothed in a black robe and hood,
takes his horrid fleshly form and begins to enjoy the hot
breakfast meal along with the rest of the family. EARL looks
at his CHILDREN. They enter the dining room and take their
seats. Resting their elbows on the table they cover their
ear.

                    EARL HAROLD PAUL
          Emma Peterson will be my new wife,
          my new wine of love. In this new
          life of immortality that you,
          Ammonothus have given to me, I choose
          Emma. Presently, she's the wife
          married to a whore monger. A lawyer
          whose name is Jacob Peterson. "A
          direct" descendant of Professor
          Jeremiah Peterson, must die. Why,
          why, why must Jacob die?

Everyone except the CHILDREN.

                    FAMILY OF EARL
          He's the descendent of Jeremiah, who
          loved, who ravished and tasted your
          wife.

                    EARL HAROLD PAUL
          Ammonothus. Does Jacob and Emma
          have children?

                    AMMONOTHUS
          Yes. Three. Two girls and one boy.

                    EARL HAROLD PAUL
          They must die!

                    AMMONOTHUS
          They are feasting at the Pancake
          Palace. Emma is not present.

                    EARL HAROLD PAUL
Jacob is there with his lover Judith
Edith.

                    AMMONOTHUS
You met Jacob's wife today at your
Plant facility. What is your horrid
plan for her?

                    EARL HAROLD PAUL
Emma Peterson is my new grape. Like
Maple Mary, I will become drunk with
her love. Intoxicated by her inner
beauty, her loveliness and her
magnificent curvaceous design.

                    AMMONOTHUS
...Emma Peterson must die. She is
married to your descendant. Romancing
her...Is fruitless.

                    EARL HAROLD PAUL
So very wrong you are my Wraith
Master. I need to become the channel
from which her river of passion flows.
I will to channel all of my love and
lust to her and only her...Don't
touch her!

                    AMMONOTHUS
As you wish!

                    CHARLES GIBBONS
Mr. Earl my wife and I would like to
know about our son Nathan. I don't
know where he is. He has run away
form his household. He needs to be
put to death for his refusal to accept
the immortality I have received from
our Master.

                    EARL HAROLD PAUL
He has his own free will. You would
go against his will and have our
Master force immortality upon your
son?

                    CHARLES GIBBONS
By force indeed. You don't approve?

EARL ignores CHARLES. The CHILDREN uncover their ears.

                    CHARLES GIBBONS (CONT'D)
I'll find and kill him myself.

EARL HAROLD PAUL
When you find your adopted runaway
son, who is over eighteen. He's
thirty. He's a man. Not a child.
Nevertheless, what you do to your
adopted son is your business.

He looks over at the CHILDREN. They cover their ears. They
don't want to. They never want to. They obey anyway.

EARL HAROLD PAUL (CONT'D)
After your horrid pleasure with your
boy is fulfilled, find another place
of employment, Charles Judas Gibbons.
You were once very angry at my late
father in law for his parents'
treatment of your ancestors. Now
you wish to make your adopted son a
slave of immortality? I'm the only
murderer in this house. I alone am
the *Finger of God*, to strike down
all the adulterers...

CHARLES GIBBONS
Yes. Mr. Paul.

EARL HAROLD PAUL
Is that clear?

CHARLES GIBBONS
Yes. Mr. Earl Harold Paul.

EARL HAROLD PAUL
Charles, unless I give you the
permission to take another life, I
am the only person who may murder
and live under this roof.

CHARLES GIBBONS
Yes. Mr. Paul.

EARL HAROLD PAUL
Ammonothus the Wraith Man has even
submitted his horrid acts of violence
to be under my control.

CHARLES GIBBONS
I want my adopted son Nathan to
experience this wonderful the absence
of peace we all share in this
household.

                    EARL HAROLD PAUL
          I assure you the absence of peace I
          feel is no more pleasurable than the
          lost of Ammonothus's father Ammontai
          who at this moment since centuries
          long ago is serving his eternal
          sentence in the Hell of Hells...the
          place called Tartarus. This life of
          immortality for me holds terrible
          pain.

                    CHARLES GIBBONS
          I love to kill. I love it I tell
          you. I learned this horrid fun from
          you. Remember?

EARL'S eyes begin to shed tears. Tear drops leave his eyes
and float to the ceiling.

                    EARL HAROLD PAUL
          You're sick. Murder is not joyous.
          Not a day goes by I wish I would
          have made a better choice in dealing
          with my Maple Mary and her lover
          Professor. You're sick Charles.

                    CHARLES GIBBONS
          So. This household and all of the
          children you've brought into this
          world whose mothers have left you
          for one reason or another. For what
          purpose?

                    EARL HAROLD PAUL
          To make me happy. To ease the pain
          I've caused myself in this horrid
          life I've lived all these many years.

He places his hands in his face. He weeps. His tears escape
the cracks between his fingers and float to the ceiling. He
takes his hands away and the tears, like rain, defy gravity
until both of his hands are dry.

                    CHARLES GIBBONS
          My son displeases me. He dishonored
          me by running away. I adopted him.
          His hatred of me must be punished by
          death.

                    EARL HAROLD PAUL
          You fool. You idiot fool. Look at
          me. My tears. They run from me as
          if in terror. Ammonothus. Tell him
          why.

                    AMMONOTHUS
          The stench of his wickedness. The
          odor of his iniquity. The immortality
          of my wretchedness that I have given
          him causes this phenomenon.

                    CHARLES GIBBONS
          Doesn't happen to me!

                    AMMONOTHUS
          I did not bless you. I did not lay
          my hands of dark eternal light upon
          you.

                    EARL HAROLD PAUL
          I gave you a portion of my dark light.
          You don't have it fully. So, you
          must obey me.

                    CHARLES GIBBONS
          If I choose not to obey you?

AMMONOTHUS looks at CHARLES. His tears run down his cheek
as he looks at AMMONOTHUS then at EARL.

                    CHARLES GIBBONS (CONT'D)
          I understand.

                    EARL HAROLD PAUL
          I will go about my business of murder
          today and then ravish the wife of
          Jacob Peterson. We will have
          children. What a wonderful happy
          family we all will continue to be.
          For all time. For centuries to come.

EARL bows his head for a moment as he whispers these words
to MAPLE MARY in prayer.

                    EARL HAROLD PAUL (CONT'D)
          Maple Mary forgive me for I will
          continue to sin. Please don't be
          jealous. I will marry Emma. She
          will take the place of you in my
          heart for a moment in time. Maple
          Mary you must be patient! I'll take
          my own life soon, and return to you.

While EARL meditates his CHILDREN uncover their ears.

                    EARL HAROLD PAUL (CONT'D)
          I will bring more...Innocent ears
          are covered. Innocent ears are
          covered!

His CHILDREN obey him reluctantly.

                    EARL HAROLD PAUL (CONT'D)
          Sons and daughters into this family
          through the womb of Emma Peterson.
          Ok, children!

The CHILDREN uncover their ears. They begin to eat.

                    EARL HAROLD PAUL (CONT'D)
          How glorious it would have been for
          each and every one of you to have
          had Maple Mary as your mother. I
          regret that it never happened.

                    CHILDREN OF EARL
          Yes, father.

                    EARL HAROLD PAUL
          Although I do find-

He only has to look at his CHILDREN and they know what to
do. They slam their spoons on the table and quickly obey.

                    EARL HAROLD PAUL (CONT'D)
          -Emma attractive, her beauty alone
          is not my reason for allowing her
          into my life. Professor Peterson
          took Maple Mary from me and ravished
          her. Now I will ravish a wife from
          one of his descendants. I will give
          Emma immortality. She will become
          my new Maple Mary.

He smiles at his CHILDREN. They continue eating their meal.
Some use butter on their oatmeal and raisins while others
just milk and sugar to sweeten their breakfast to their
liking.

                    EARL HAROLD PAUL (CONT'D)
          I am finished with my breakfast Mr.
          Gibbons.

                    CHARLES GIBBONS
          Yes, sir!

                    EARL HAROLD PAUL
          Bring me a sharper knife. I'll need
          to take it with me.

                    CHARLES GIBBONS
          Right away I'll take your plate Mr.
          Paul.

                    EARL HAROLD PAUL
          And you might want to take this knife.
          I cut myself again, I keep beating
          myself on my legs. Nasty painful
          habit!

                    CHARLES GIBBONS
          Not a problem Mr. Paul I'll get you
          another one. Manny? First aid kit!

MANNY a 60 year old Irish man who became employed in the
service of Mr. Paul on October 1, 1900. An immortal who is
CHARLES'S chief assistant among the staff of the EARL HAROLD
PAUL estate.

                    MANNY THE SERVANT
          Right away sir!

MANNY reveals his first aid bag with a big red cross. The
kit was already over his shoulder. He reaches inside for
bandages. Another servant hands MANNY hot towels. He gives
the hot towels and dry bandages to Butler CHARLES GIBBONS
who assists EARL. EARL takes what he needs and hands the
blood-soiled towels to CHARLES who tosses them into a small
laundry basket held by another servant.

                    AMMONOTHUS
          Emma Peterson has just been released
          by the authorities. She is alone at
          her establishment.

                    EARL HAROLD PAUL
          Emma's Tailor & Bizarre Costume Shop?

                    AMMONOTHUS
          Yes! I'll be along shortly, after
          breakfast.

EARL gets up from his chair. Seeing EARL get up, everyone,
out of respect, stands to their feet.

                    EARL HAROLD PAUL
          Thank you my Master. I'll get changed
          and be on my way.

                    CHILDREN OF EARL
          Have a good day, father!

                    EARL HAROLD PAUL
          You too children have a wonderful
          day!

                                        FADE OUT:

FADE IN:

48 <u>INT. BUFFALO PANCAKE PALACE -- MORNING</u>   **48**

Seated at the table is JACOB PETERSON a 38 year old lawyer
who owns a firm, his children SAMANTHA 10 years old, BILLY
14 years old, LISA 12 years old, and his lover JUDITH EDITH
HOPKINS, a redhead model type who is 28 years old and is
also a lawyer. With bowed heads and plates filled with
pancakes and tall glasses of milk, JACOB offers a prayer.

>   JACOB PETERSON
>   Never again...

>   SAMANTHA
>   Where is mother?

>   LISA
>   Why are we having breakfast again
>   without mother?

>   BILLY
>   Are we running away from mother or
>   Ammonothus the Wraith Man again?

>   JACOB PETERSON
>   Never again...

>   JUDITH EDITH HOPKINS
>   Your father is trying to pray for
>   our meal children.

>   BILLY
>   You're obsessed with Ammonothus aren't
>   you father? I hope he comes here
>   and teaches you a lesson for cheating
>   on mother.

>   JUDITH EDITH HOPKINS
>   It's just not polite to talk to your
>   father in that manner.

>   JACOB PETERSON
>   Never again will our family be
>   haunted...

>   LISA
>   If you'd just love mother...

>   SAMANTHA
>   I'm not haunted!

                    BILLY
None of us are haunted by the
Ammonothus the Wraith Man. It's
just father who won't stop sleeping
with you Judith. Why don't you just
leave? You're not a part of our
family.

          JUDITH EDITH HOPKINS
Hold your tongue young man!

          JACOB PETERSON
We will never be hunted down ever
again!

                    LISA
I'm not afraid of Ammonothus the
Wraith Man. Why are you father?

                    BILLY
Because he's living in sin!

          JUDITH EDITH HOPKINS
How dare you judge your father!

                SAMANTHA
How dare you try to take the place
of our beloved mother! Now can we
just order? I need to eat, but I do
wish mother was here. Where is
mother?

          JACOB PETERSON
Earl Harold Paul wants your mother.
He just wants to have his way with
her.

                    BILLY
In the same way you are having your
way with Judith Edith your lover?

          JUDITH EDITH HOPKINS
You just can't speak that way to
your father. Do you understand?

          JACOB PETERSON
It's ok. I love you children. I
will rescue this household of ours
from all evil.

          JUDITH EDITH HOPKINS
Jacob? What are you talking about?
What are you saying?

JACOB smiles a little. He takes out his 9mm and shoots all
of his CHILDREN and his lover JUDITH. He places the gun on
the table. He bows his head and mumbles to himself.

He repeats the same words...

> JACOB PETERSON
> The Wraith Man Ammonothus, Ammonothus
> made me do it! I told you he made
> me do it! He made me do it! Oh yes
> he did!

CUSTOMERS of the pancake restaurant scream as they run out
of the double doors into the street. JACOB is still mumbling
the same words.

> JACOB PETERSON (V.O.) (CONT'D)
> The Wraith Man Ammonothus, Ammonothus
> made me do it! I told you he made
> me do it! He made me do it! Oh yes
> he did!

DISSOLVE TO:

49 INT. BUFFALO PANCAKE PALACE -- MOMENTS LATER   49

JACOB is handcuffed sitting at the table mumbling to himself.
Buffalo detectives, athletic in appearance looking like the
stars of a television cop melodrama, surround the table where
he is sitting batting his eyes appearing to be in a trance.

Detectives ANITA CRUZ a Puerto Rican age 30 and her secret
lover and partner LAWRENCE WILLIAMS an African American age
47 who is married to an FBI Agent. The detectives arrive
with their Lieutenant JACQUELINE JENKINS, an African American.
She is 40 years old. Lt. JENKINS kneels down and looks into
the eyes as JACOB as he continues to mumble to himself, but
this time he raises his voice.

> JACOB PETERSON
> The Wraith Man Ammonothus, Ammonothus
> made me do it! I told you he made
> me do it! He made me do it! Oh yes
> he did!

Tears begin to flow down JACOB'S face.

DISSOLVE TO:

50 INT. BUFFALO PANCAKE PALACE -- MOMENTS LATER   50

JACOB is being photographed by police at the table. More
officers arrive in the establishment. Black Suburbans are
parked outside of the large glass windows of the restaurant.

                    JACOB PETERSON (V.O.)
          The Wraith Man Ammonothus, Ammonothus
          made me do it!

Walking towards the table the FBI agents listen to the words
of the distressed JACOB PETERSON. Agents Carla Vivian Van
Holt-Williams enters, whose husband is a Buffalo Police
detective. She is a blond, petite woman 31 years old. She
looks over at her husband who is standing too close to ANITA
CRUZ. CRUZ moves away from LAWRENCE and shakes her hand and
the other FBI agents who follow CARLA. Agents ROGER MICKEY
MADISON, age 33, NIGEL OSCAR KNOLL age 35, and FELIX FRANKLIN
HAYES age 29.

                    JACOB PETERSON (V.O.) (CONT'D)
          I told you he made me do it! He
          made me do it! Oh yes he did!

JACOB's eyes are red and filled with tears as the FBI Agents
and detectives look into his eyes. His family is taken by
the Coroner's office. JACOB bows his head then lifts it up
to the ceiling as he repeats his words.

CARLA, ROGER, FELIX, LAWRENCE, ANITA and Lt. JENKINS are
seated around the table studying JACOB'S demeanor and taking
it among themselves. JACOB'S eyes are fixed on the image he
sees in front of him as he looks straight ahead. AMMONOTHUS
THE WRAITH MAN is at the head of the table. He does not
even see the officers. They are blurred in his vision. He
only notices how beastly the face of AMMONOTHUS appears to
him.

JACOB smiles. More tears flow from his eyes. Suddenly, his
tears begin to defy gravity at the astonishment of the law
enforcement in the restaurant. The officers and agents are
amazed at the phenomenon.

JACOB begins to whisper to himself.

                                        DISSOLVE TO:

51 **EXT. BUFFALO PANCAKE PALACE** -- CONTINUOUS   51

No one sees AMMONOTHUS THE WRAITH MAN except for JACOB. He
looks back at the Pancake Palace as he is placed into a black
Suburban. AMMONOTHUS is standing on the inside of the
restaurant looking through the glass window at JACOB. JACOB
still in shock stares back.

APPLEGATE NEWS vans arrive at the scene. Reporter APPLEGATE
stands in front of the establishment with her crew. She
talks in front of two cameras. The sixteen-foot AMMONOTHUS
reveals himself in all of his beastly wretchedness and horrid
glory. The CROWD is shocked, amazed and frightened.

Hundreds cheer. Others weep in the presence of AMMONOTHUS.
Their tears fall but defy gravity. Like raindrops they fall
but then ascend into the sky forming a whirlwind of water.
In the midst of the whirlwind AMMONOTHUS THE WRAITH MAN
ascends until he reaches the clouds. The clouds begin to
form into a tornado. The entire sky grows dark with clouds
that enter into the tornado.

Then he ascends higher into the clouds. AMMONOTHUS disappears
in a blinding light. This light causes a chain reaction of
electrical light through the morning clouds.

The clouds become a dancing fireworks display of colorful
rays of electrical light. The FBI Suburbans and police
detective Crown Victoria's drive off. The law enforcement
officers look to the skies as they drive away.

The clouds in the sky over the Pancake Palace twirl like a
tornado. When the tornado's winds touch the rooftop of the
establishment it begins to dissipate. PEOPLE line the streets
while OFFICERS hold the CROWD back.

52 <u>INT. EARL'S HUMMER LIMO -- MORNING</u>   52

Passing by the Buffalo Pancake Palace, no one recognizes
EARL as he presses down his window. He watches the crowd as
they look up at the dancing spectacle of light in the morning
clouds. JAMES TOWNSEND, his life long friend, is the limo
driver. Other men in EHP Waste Management dark green
jumpsuits and matching baseball caps sit near him including
BOB KNOLL and TIM HAYES. JAMES presses down the window that
separates his driver cab from the passenger section.

                    JAMES TOWNSEND
               We will finally crush all the
               adulterers of this city. I'm glad
               you went to Egypt in 1899.

                    EARL HAROLD PAUL
               The crowd loves Ammonothus the Wraith
               Man and the destruction he brings.
               But at last they will all be punished
               because of the adulterous lives they
               live.

                    JAMES TOWNSEND
               Ammonothus the Wraith Man will punish
               them for their sins.

                    EARL HAROLD PAUL
               In all of his horrid wretched glory.
               Are the incinerators at the Waste
               Plant ready to handle such a task?

          JAMES TOWNSEND
The citizens of Buffalo will be
stacked twelve feet high in the
streets. Your garbage truck fleet
will pick them up.

          EARL HAROLD PAUL
Good. We will finally cleanse this
city of its wicked wretched filth.
For their sins of adultery they will
all be purged by the fires of my
plant's incinerators.

          JAMES TOWNSEND
Nothing can stop you and Ammonothus
the Wraith Man.

          EARL HAROLD PAUL
Except for her. She promised never
to leave me alone.

EARL whispers to himself.

          EARL HAROLD PAUL (CONT'D)
She promised never ever to leave me
alone.

          JAMES TOWNSEND
Who?

          EARL HAROLD PAUL
I can sense her peaceful presence.
Her soul is filled with songs, hymns
suites. Her melodies are in my mind
still.

          JAMES TOWNSEND
Who?

          BOB KNOLL
Who else.

          TIM HAYES
She died long ago Earl.

          JAMES TOWNSEND
My cousin?

          JAMES & EARL
Darlene Bainbridge!

          EARL HAROLD PAUL
Darlene Bainbridge.
          (MORE)

                    EARL HAROLD PAUL (CONT'D)
        Her merciful spirit watches over
        this city. I'd love...I'd love to
        see her again. James? Let every
        one out at the Plant they have work
        to do. Then, drive me past Emma's
        Costume Shop.

                    JAMES TOWNSEND
        Yes Earl.

53 <u>EXT. EARL'S HUMMER LIMO</u> -- CONTINUOUS   53

EARL'S limo passes through the crowds of downtown Buffalo.
His tears flow upward into the sky. He presses up the window.
His Hummer limo merges with the maze of other vehicles.

                                        FADE OUT:

FADE IN:

54 <u>EXT. EMMA'S TAILOR & BIZARRE COSTUME SHOP</u> -- DAY   54

The sign on the front door reads: closed until noon. It is
now 11:00 am. The electronic wall clock inside the wall is
clearly seen from the outside. Crown Victorias and Suburbans
drive by with Agent ROGER, his fellow agents, Lt. JACQUELINE
JENKINS and her detectives. The caravan stops in front of
the establishment.

They all get out of their vehicles and walk up to the door.
Lt. JENKINS knocks on the door.

No answer.

EMMA is in the rear. Door bell reads "sorry". The note is
in EMMA'S handwriting. Two pieces of Scotch tape are over
the door bell with a neatly placed green memo "stick em".
The note is folded in half. They look at the clock and their
watches. They get back into the automobiles and pull off.

                                        DISSOLVE TO:

55 <u>EXT. EMMA'S TAILOR & BIZARRE COSTUME SHOP</u>   55

The clock on the wall reads 11:45 am.

Mr. PAUL'S hummer limo stops in front of the Costume Shop.
EARL presses down the window. EMMA sees him. She opens the
door and stands in the doorway and smiles.

EARL gets out while JAMES TOWNSEND holds the door of the
limo.

56 <u>INT. EMMA'S TAILOR & BIZARRE COSTUME SHOP</u>   56

His confidence and wretchedness moves her deeply. EMMA
believes all the rumors surrounding him. "The mass murderer
who puts the adulterers to death." She can see into his pain.
She is overcome with his natural scent. She is not afraid
of him. EARL'S immortality gives off a scent of death.

She brings out a cape and places it over his shoulders.
EMMA wraps her arms around him. They look into each others
eyes for a moment.

                    EMMA PETERSON
        You smell.

                    EARL HAROLD PAUL
        I smell?

                    EMMA PETERSON
        Like death!

                    EARL HAROLD PAUL
        I wouldn't know. I haven't died
        yet.

EMMA smiles.

                    EMMA PETERSON
        This is my humble Shop.

                    EARL HAROLD PAUL
        Nice place. Costumes? Your passion.

EMMA lets her eyes roam around the room so EARL can get a
good look at her pretty eyes. She smiles.

She whispers to herself while looking deep into his eyes.

                    EMMA PETERSON
        The way you smell...

                    EARL HAROLD PAUL
        What did you say?

                    EMMA PETERSON
        My husband is a lawyer. I think
        yeah, I told you that. Maybe I
        didn't.

                    EARL HAROLD PAUL
        Where is he now?

                    EMMA PETERSON
        At this moment he's having breakfast
        with his lover and my children.
        But, it's over between us.

                    EARL HAROLD PAUL
        Emma? Spend the day with me?

                    EMMA PETERSON
        Lead on! You wicked wretched man.

They leave the shop. The clock reads 12:00 noon. She tries
to get him to carry her by jumping in his arms. EARL carries
her to the limo while JAMES stands by the door of the limo.
She kisses him on the cheek and gets inside first then he
enters the vehicle.

                    EMMA PETERSON (V.O.) (CONT'D)
        Mr. Paul make love to me before
        breakfast. You've had breakfast.
        Did you have fruit? No? No.
        Well...have some fruit, it's good
        for you!

His BELT and her BRA are thrown from the sunroof.

                    EMMA PETERSON (V.O.) (CONT'D)
        Earl! You're...Oh! Oh so so wicked!

The Hummer pulls off with her HANDS extended from the sunroof.

55 INT. EMMA'S TAILOR & BIZARRE COSTUME SHOP   55

The clock reads 12:05 pm. The store hours sign is in the
window. The open side is facing the officers as they pull
up in their Suburbans and Crown Victorias. Lt. JENKINS, her
Detectives, Agent MADISON and his Agents knock on the door
at the same time. They look at their watches and the clock
on the wall. They see the sign. They drop their business
cards in the mail box. The cards fall to the floor. They
enter their cars.

The FBI Suburbans and Police Crown Victorias pull off.

                                        DISSOLVE TO:

FADE IN:

56 INT. NIAGARA FALLS SEAFOOD PALACE -- EVENING   56

EMMA is dressed in a black gown. Her hair is up revealing
her lovely neck and cleavage. The onyx and gold chain she
is wearing is a gift from EARL.

He is dressed in a Hugo Boss black pin stripe suit, with a black tie and diamond cuff links and tie clip.

The waiter is the adopted son of EARL'S Butler. Nathan is his name. An African American man in his thirties although he looks like he is in his late twenties. He is dressed in a white tux. The Seafood Palace is an upscale establishment that over looks river Niagara and its magnificent falls.

EARL is seated across EMMA who takes off her wedding ring and places it in her new black purse she admires which is also a gift. EMMA'S back is toward the six 40 inch plasma screens that hang over the bar. The bartender is serving drinks to a crowd. The APPLEGATE NEWS Special Report is on. "Ammonothus Sightings". The bartender is playing *JAZZ* on satellite radio while the volume on the television is turned down so that the restaurant customers can hear the music while watching television.

                EARL HAROLD PAUL
      If he hits you again, I'll have my
      men...my employees come by your place
      and chop both of his hands off and
      take them away with your garbage.

They both laugh, just a little.

                EMMA PETERSON
      Or you could come by and chop his
      hands off. I don't allow strange
      men in my house. You could take
      both of his hands outside and your
      men...your employees could then take
      them away with the rest of the garbage
      in this city.

                EARL HAROLD PAUL
      I've always desired to have a woman
      just like you around the house to
      care for me.

She smiles, kind of.

                EARL HAROLD PAUL (CONT'D)
      I'm serious. No I am being very
      truthful with you.

                EMMA PETERSON
      How many children do you have?

                EARL HAROLD PAUL
      I have six boys and seven girls, and
      not by the same woman, unfortunately.

                    EMMA PETERSON
          Your estate must be a grand nursery.
          Where are their moms?

                    EARL HAROLD PAUL
          They've all run off with other men.

                    EMMA PETERSON
          All of them?

                    EARL HAROLD PAUL
          Afraid so except for well, I've never
          married any of them.

                    EMMA PETERSON
          Be very truthful with me. Did you
          kill them and their lovers?

                    EARL HAROLD PAUL
          I don't do that.

                    EMMA PETERSON
          Did you kill Maple Mary?

                    EARL HAROLD PAUL
          How do you know about-?

Mr. PAUL notices the APPLEGATE NEWS Special on the plasma
screens over the bar across the room. All six are on the
same channel. Reporter AGNES ANNA APPLEGATE is reporting.
EMMA keeps her eyes on EARL.

                    EARL HAROLD PAUL (CONT'D)
          Oh, you watch Agnes Anna Applegate's
          news show. Don't watch TV.

                    EMMA PETERSON
          If you don't watch TV, how would you
          know about-?

EMMA notices the plasma screen above the bartenders head.

                    EARL HAROLD PAUL
          I dine here often, sometimes when I
          want to have a meal alone and enjoy
          the view. They keep APPLEGATE NEWS
          channel on all day and all night.

EMMA notices the menu ad *"We're open 24 hours! All for you!"*

                    EMMA PETERSON
          Here in this town everyone well not
          everyone but most, I guess think
          you're some mass murderer.

> EARL HAROLD PAUL
> I've never been convicted of any
> crime. Why are you here right now?

> EMMA PETERSON
> I like you. I adore you. You're
> mysterious. You're a tabloid. You're
> rich. For some reason you desire me
> and I like the attention. I need
> the attention right now. I'd like
> to have your attention forever.

> EARL HAROLD PAUL
> Other men can give you attention.

> EMMA PETERSON
> Other men aren't you.

> EARL HAROLD PAUL
> There are other tabloid men. Richer
> tabloid men. Why me?

> EMMA PETERSON
> I love the smell of death on you.

> EARL HAROLD PAUL
> I wear Obsession For Men. Perhaps I
> should change my cologne.

> EMMA PETERSON
> You have this natural scent of death.
> Change your natural scent and I'll
> kill you!

EMMA isn't laughing she just stares into his eyes although
EARL anticipates her smile.

> EMMA PETERSON (CONT'D)
> No I am kidding. Really!

EMMA still does not smile. Nathan comes across the room
with a platter of seafood and a steak dinner for another
table near where EMMA and EARL are sitting.

> EARL HAROLD PAUL
> Nathan? Steak knife!

> NATHAN THE WAITER
> You ordered a steak and sea food
> platter Mr. Paul?

> EARL HAROLD PAUL
> No. Just let me have your steak
> knife please.

NATHAN give him the steak knife.

>   NATHAN THE WAITER
>   Your order will be right up. Sorry
>   for the wait.

>   EARL HAROLD PAUL
>   No problem thanks.

NATHAN leaves their table. EARL wraps the knife in his napkin
and hands it to EMMA.

>   EARL HAROLD PAUL (CONT'D)
>   Whenever you like. You have my
>   permission. Cut my throat. Whenever
>   you feel the urge. It just takes a
>   little nerve that's all.

>   EMMA PETERSON
>   I have your permission to cut my own
>   throat? You want me to cut my own
>   throat?

>   EARL HAROLD PAUL
>   Mine.

>   EMMA PETERSON
>   Right now?

>   EARL HAROLD PAUL
>   If you'd like.

EMMA hops on EARL'S lap. She places the knife on his throat.

>   EARL HAROLD PAUL (CONT'D)
>   Just press down hard. Don't be
>   gentle. Don't be timid. Don't be
>   afraid.

>   EMMA PETERSON
>   I'm thirsty.

She takes a sip of her glass of wine.

>   EMMA PETERSON (CONT'D)
>   Wine?

>   EARL HAROLD PAUL
>   I would rather have the sweet wine
>   of your kisses.

EMMA places the glass of wine down and takes a swallow from
the bottle then kisses EARL. Wine pours out of their mouths.

                    NATHAN THE WAITER
        Do you want a towel sir?

                    EARL HAROLD PAUL
            No, Nathan.

                    EMMA PETERSON
        Earl doesn't need a towel, my tongue
        is his towel.

EMMA begins to lick the wine off his chin. She drinks a
swallow of wine from the bottle. EMMA kisses his lips then
his forehead. EARL buries his face between her cleavage and
inhales the fragrance of her body while kissing her breast
gently.

                    EARL HAROLD PAUL
            I love your sweet scent.

                    EMMA PETERSON
        But I'm not wearing anything.

He comes up for air.

                    EARL HAROLD PAUL
        Then it's the smell of your natural
        sweet scent that I love.

                    EMMA PETERSON
        I love how death smells on you. My
        obsession with you, is the smell of
        death!

EARL looks into EMMA'S eyes. She smiles. He smiles back.

                    EARL HAROLD PAUL
        Yet, you own a Tailor & Bizarre
        Costume Shop. Why not a mortuary?

They both drink from the same bottle of wine. She drinks
first not noticing her murdered family being reported by
APPLEGATE on the plasma screen above the bar. He tries not
to look at the news report.

                    EMMA PETERSON
        Mortician? The funning thing is
        when I was just a teenager, I thought
        I'd work what is now called Weeping
        Willow & Eternal Pines Mortuary
        Cemetery. Little did I know that
        I'd be related through marriage to
        Noah Peterson, the owner of Weeping
        Willow Cemetery.

>   EARL HAROLD PAUL
>   Yes of course, Noah Peterson. The
>   Peterson Family are quite ambitious.
>   He's been dead now for ten years I
>   think.

>   EMMA PETERSON
>   The *cheater*...He died tragically
>   five years ago. Did you kill him?

NATHAN the waiter walks by with the bill in his notebook
organizer. He has all of his business documents, such as
extra pens, pencils, blank order forms he keeps neatly, his
notebook folder. He can hardly wait to fill the table that
EARL and EMMA are occupying with more paying customers.

>   EARL HAROLD PAUL
>   ...N-no!

As he stops at EARL'S table, he notices other regulars who
want the same table. He nods his head at his other guess at
the entrance of the restaurant before looking down at EARL
and his ravishing date.

>   EARL HAROLD PAUL (CONT'D)
>   Nathan, I'm ready to pay.

She whispers in his ear but loud enough for NATHAN to hear.

>   EMMA PETERSON
>   EARL, I'm ready to play.

>   NATHAN THE WAITER
>   Allowing you two to play requires-

>   EMMA PETERSON
>   What Nathan?

>   NATHAN THE WAITER
>   Tip! A large, a very large
>   substantial tip for allowing you two
>   to perform the most perverted show
>   that I've ever allowed at my table.

>   EMMA PETERSON
>   Nathan, you're rude. You're a rude
>   waiter.

He hands NATHAN three new one-hundred dollar bills. Two of
the bills are stuck together.

>   NATHAN THE WAITER
>   Two bills?
>   (MORE)

NATHAN THE WAITER (CONT'D)
Oh no, three hundred dollars. Thanks,
Mr. Paul. Ma-lady? Tip? Tip tip
tip!

EMMA PETERSON
Rude man you are! Don't be hatin'
Nathan!

EARL HAROLD PAUL
The Three hundred dollars was for
our meal, the wine and the show.

NATHAN THE WAITER
Sunday brunches around this place
just wouldn't be the same without
you and your tips Earl! Next Sunday
then.

EARL HAROLD PAUL
Of course, as always. Your father
asks about you.

NATHAN THE WAITER
My natural father is dead.

EARL HAROLD PAUL
Yes. But your adopted father still
thinks of you as a boy. He thinks
of you as his little adopted kid.

NATHAN THE WAITER
You know the deal with Charles. I
appreciate you not telling him where
I work.

EARL HAROLD PAUL
And I'll never tell him Nathan. You
have your free will. Immortality
can not be rammed down someone's
throat.

NATHAN THE WAITER
I am not your judge. I just love to
serve people. Make my guests feel
warm. I'm here to serve you and
make you feel happy that you dined
here and not anywhere else.

EARL HAROLD PAUL
That's why I come here. There's a
peace that overshadows you. Very
strange I can't understand it.

>   NATHAN THE WAITER
>   My humanity is filled with peace.

>   EARL HAROLD PAUL
>   Immortality thrills me although I
>   have no peace. I will always respect
>   your life's choice to remain as you
>   are.

EMMA reaches out her hand. Only while conversing with NATHAN
she tries acting and talking with a *"ghetto"* attitude which
embarrasses EARL.

>   EMMA PETERSON
>   Want my autograph? Alright with me
>   I'll use your pen.

She takes his pen. He takes it right back.

>   NATHAN THE WAITER
>   Lady? Have a wonderful afternoon.

>   EMMA PETERSON
>   Afternoon, waiter boy. Wah' cha'
>   starin' at? Bus this goddamn table!

>   EARL HAROLD PAUL
>   Get up. Get up! Thanks Nathan.

EMMA whispers. She puts her head against his. They look in
each other's eyes. She kisses both of his eyes and lips.

>   EMMA PETERSON
>   Carry your sweetness, Earl?

EARL'S wretched heart melts for a moment. Realizing he's
whipped, he carries her through the restaurant. Two bus
boys perform their duties at NATHAN'S table while he greets
his next group of guests.

>   EMMA PETERSON (CONT'D)
>   Oh Nathan? Work! Work work work!

She enjoys his kisses while being carried. He notices the
APPLEGATE NEWS FLASH. She does not. Reporter AGNES ANNA
APPLEGATE shows video footage of the Pancake Palace
Restaurant. EARL watches JACOB being carried away by the
Buffalo Police department. He continues to carry her to his
waiting Hummer limo. Finally, she sees through the window.
The live broadcast shows her children in body bags being
handled by the Coroners as they zip the bags over the lifeless
bodies. She sees JACOB being carried away with Police.
EMMA covers her mouth in shock.

EARL carries her back to the window.

FADE OUT:

FADE IN:

57 EXT. WEEPING WILLOW & ETERNAL PINES CEMETERY --   57
EVENING

The funeral becomes a montage of dissolves capturing the
emotions of friends and loved ones of EMMA PETERSON. EMMA
kneels down in front of an open grave. She casts dirt on
top of her head. She weeps as the METHODIST PASTOR, an Afro-
American minister at the Buffalo Methodist Cathedral of Mercy
speaks and the crowd listens.

DISSOLVE TO:

EMMA kisses the dirt and throws it on the descending coffins.

DISSOLVE TO:

EMMA is comforted by her METHODIST PASTOR. He leaves as the
Buffalo Police detectives LAWRENCE WILLIAMS, ANITA CRUZ, and
Lt. JACQUELINE JENKINS kneel down to comfort her. FBI Agents
CARLA VAN HOLT-WILLIAMS, FELIX, ROGER MICKEY MADISON stand
in the distance dressed in black suits with sunglasses.

DISSOLVE TO:

With the sun going down the METHODIST PASTOR and Lt. JENKINS
try to stand her to her feet with the cemetery workers behind
them. When she refuses, they leave her alone at the grave
site except for the Weeping Willow employees who take shovels
and pour dirt over the coffins.

DISSOLVE TO:

EMMA gently pats the dirt over the grave site and places
three flowers in the dirt as the tombstones are placed in
position. She touches the names of her three children carved
in the tombstones. The Weeping Willow employees pat her on
her shoulder and walk away leaving her at the grave site.

DISSOLVE TO:

58 EXT. WEEPING WILLOW & ETERNAL PINES CEMETERY -- NIGHT   58

The night sky is filled with stars and the last ray of sun
fades. The wind blows the Weeping Willow trees of the
cemetery park. The LEAVES fall all around EMMA like a small
tornado. The LEAVES come to rest. She looks around noticing
as three black Suburbans drive off followed by two black
Crown Victorias and a black Dodge R/T Charger.

As they drive off the property they turn their headlights on.

EMMA looks back at her children's tombstones while wiping her eyes. The spirits of her children BILLY, SAMANTHA, and LISA rise out of their graves from their chest up. Shaking off the dirt from their hair and eyes they smile at her.

She smiles back. They stop smiling and just stare at her. As they speak she can hardly hear their words as if their voices are coming from a different dimension. While they converse with her their VOICES grow louder.

> BILLY,SAMANTHA, &LISA
> Mother why do you love a murderer?

> EMMA PETERSON
> Children?

> BILLY,SAMANTHA, &LISA
> Mother why do you love a murderer?

> EMMA PETERSON
> Children? I'm so sorry your father
> did this to you. Come come to your
> mother. Let me hold you one last
> time?

> BILLY,SAMANTHA, &LISA
> Mother? Cut off his head. Bring it
> to us. Bring it to us in a silver
> canister.

> EMMA PETERSON
> Children! Come to me. Let me hold
> you in my arms.

EMMA laughs hysterically. She has just heard what they asked her to do. She laughs because she doesn't understand, because she needs to humor herself. But, consciously, she does not know why she's laughing. She wants to cry but can't so she laughs with tears in her eyes.

> BILLY,SAMANTHA, &LISA
> Cut off his head. Bring it to us.
> Bring it to us in a silver canister!

With tears running down her face, *is this real*, she wonders?

> EMMA PETERSON
> Children! Stop it.

BILLY, SAMANTHA and LISA continue with their demands, angering her.

                    EMMA PETERSON (CONT'D)
          Stop it! Stop it now. Children? I
          said shut up. Shut up!

BILLY, SAMANTHA and LISA do not listen. They only grow more
passionate in their demands, repeating over and over
continually. The kids want the head of Earl Harold Paul's
head in a silver canister, but EMMA thinks they want their
father's head instead.

                    EMMA PETERSON (CONT'D)
          You're going to listen. You are not
          being very obedient. It is time for
          a *"time out"*. I want you to listen
          to me. Obey! Obey your mother!

They don't listen. They continue. EMMA weeps.

                    EMMA PETERSON (CONT'D)
          Earl Harold Paul? I need you.

Suddenly, the TOMBSTONES fall over! The Spirits of her
children disappear. EMMA watches the dirt being moved around
their graves as the kids dig their way back into their
coffins.

A silver CANISTER falls from the sky fifty yards away from
EMMA. She notices that the sky is raining silver canisters
in the distance. The *rain* is approaching her direction.
She sees heads roll out but can't see the person's face.

Several canisters roll by her. All around her the heads of
MR. PAUL begin to fill the cemetery. Out of a canister EMMA
picks up the HEAD of EARL covered in German Wolf's HAIRS
soaking in goat's MILK. Lifting the head of her lover into
her arms she kisses his lips while other canisters continue
to fall from the gray celestial clouds over her in the full
moonlight. The clouds roll across the starlit sky.

EARL looks at her with loving eyes and a half smile. He
vomits goats milk and German Wolf Shepherd hairs. She wipes
his mouth face and fixes his hair. He smiles a little more.
He takes a breath of clean air. Exhaling he coughs a little.
She kisses his eyes and mouth.

When EARL speaks, his words EMMA believes.

                    EARL HAROLD PAUL
          I'll never kill our child! Emma?
          I'll never harm our son.

Frightened, she runs away with his HEAD in her arms as
hundreds of other canisters rain down from above. She drops
EARL'S head when a CANISTER hits her on the forehead.

She weeps and runs faster, but in large circles. EMMA notices that the entire cemetery is starting to fill up with the HEAD of EARL inside the CANISTERS of German Wolf's HAIRS and goat's MILK.

EMMA runs back to her children's grave site.

> EMMA PETERSON
> Children? Billy? Samantha? Lisa?
> Stop it! Please, please stop!

She notices WRITING beginning to be carved into the tombstones.

"MURDER OUR DEAREST BROTHER GROWING INSIDE OF YOU or Earl Harold Paul WILL."

Fewer canisters fall from the sky. EARL'S HEAD rolls close to her side again where she is kneeling by her children's graves. It is covered in the HAIRS of a German Wolf Shepherd. Goat's milk pours out of his mouth.

Then the images of BILLY, SAMANTHA, and LISA come out of the stone. Their HEADS are not made of flesh, but of the same TEXTURE of the tombstones.

> BILLY,SAMANTHA, &LISA
> Kill our beloved brother Mother or
> Earl Harold Paul will!

> EMMA PETERSON
> I am not pregnant!

She gets up and walks down the hill, sobbing.

The spirits of BILLY, SAMANTHA and LISA escape their coffins. The children slither along on their bellies like Diamondbacks after her. EMMA runs into a tree. EMMA falls backwards into the arms of who she believes to be her lover EARL.

59 EXT. TWIN ANGELIC TOMBSTONE STATURE SITE -- CONTINUOUS 59

Startled, she calms down and begins to cry in his arms as her children move along on their bellies beneath the feet of AMMONOTHUS. She buries her face in his neck. When she looks up she finds herself in the arms of the sixteen-foot AMMONOTHUS the WRAITH MAN. She faints. He carries her in his arms.

The spirits of BILLY, SAMANTHA, and LISA crawl backwards as fast as they can to their graves. Digging their way into the ground beneath their tombstones that stand upright.

AMMONOTHUS lays EMMA down over the graves of her children.

60 <u>EXT. EMMA'S CHILDREN TOMB GRAVESTONES</u> -- NIGHT   **60**

The moonlight shines through the wooded cemetery. EMMA
unconsciously begins wiping her face. She feels fall from
the sky on her forehead. Drops of blood fall down out of
the sky and land on EMMA'S forehead.

Through the rays of the moonlight, AMMONOTHUS sees hundreds
of PLACENTA BAGS of unborn children fall from the sky. It's
a cold windy night. The temperature drops and the warmth of
the baby boys inside of each bag causes the release of STEAM.

Frightened AMMONOTHUS runs and climbs a tree as it begins to
rain placentas. The unborn children are all the same age.
Seven months old. Emma is laying down on her children's
graves. A placenta lands beside her. With her eyes closed
she rolls her head to her right side.

LIGHT escapes out of the bag as LITTLE BOO BOO, the seven
month old unborn child rips open the bloody sack and stands
over EMMA'S face.

                    LITTLE BOO BOO
          Momma! Momma? Dada won't kill me,
          my dearest Dada loves me.

The illuminated LITTLE BOO BOO kisses EMMA as she awakes and
sees what she knows is her child.

                    EMMA PETERSON
          I won't. I am not pregnant.

EMMA feels her stomach while she whispers to herself.

                    EMMA PETERSON (CONT'D)
          Am I?

                    LITTLE BOO BOO
          Dada loves me. Do you love me? I'm
          inside you momma.

                    EMMA PETERSON
          Yes I love you.

EMMA tearfully nods her head. Suddenly, PLACENTA BAGS rip
open as hundreds of illuminated unborn seven-month old BABY
BOYS run quickly toward her. They all sound and look exactly
like LITTLE BOO BOO.

                    UNBORN BABY BOYS (V.O.)
          Ma ma! I'm in your tummy. Ma ma?

She sees AMMONOTHUS the WRAITH MAN in the tree above her.
She runs away as fast as she can as it continues to rain

down placentas. Other unborn babies rip open their bloody
sacks and run after her dragging their sacks behind them.
EMMA runs past her car. Running down Weeping Willow Cemetery
Road to Main Street, she sees a car approaching.

AMMONOTHUS leaves the tree and charges after EMMA who screams.

                    EMMA PETERSON
          Freak of nature! Get away from me.

The illuminated BABIES stop running after EMMA. LITTLE BOO
BOO and the illuminated BABIES choose to chase AMMONOTHUS
instead to the top of other Weeping Willow trees. AMMONOTHUS
the WRAITH MAN in the moonlight howls his horrid cry.
Finally, it stops raining placentas under the foggy moonlight.
The CLOUDS and MIST begin clearing.

61 <u>EXT. WEEPING WILLOW CEMETERY ROAD</u> -- CONTINUOUS   61

As the car comes closer to her she sees that it is slowing
down. EMMA faints in the path of the brand new government-
tagged, triple black Dodge R/T Charger.

FBI Agent CARLA WILLIAMS gets out of her car and kicks an
empty silver canister to the side of the road. When CARLA
helps EMMA to her feet, EMMA faints in her arms.

                                        FADE OUT:

FADE IN:

62 <u>INT. AGENT CARLA'S R/T DODGE CHARGER</u> -- MOMENTS LATER   62

EMMA slowly regains her consciousness and looks over at a
woman in her middle thirties. When Agent VAN HOLT-WILLIAMS
presses her foot on the gas pedal, the leaves form small
tornadoes of their own through a residential area of Buffalo
adjacent to the Weeping Willow Cemetery Park. A tear runs
down EMMA'S face. She notices that she has no trace of blood
on her except for dirt in her hair. She remembers putting
dirt in her as the three caskets of her children were lowered
in the ground.

                    CARLA VIVIAN VAN HOLT-WILLIAMS
          You're in the good hands of the FBI.
          Mrs. Emma Peterson I presume. Mam?
          I am Agent Carla Vivian Van Holt-
          Williams.

EMMA is exhausted emotionally, but she notices other silver
canisters along the roadside. Carla notices them too.

63 <u>EXT. AGENT CARLA'S DODGE R/T CHARGER</u> -- CONTINUOUS   63

CARLA stops the car and gets out. She sees a Peter-Built
Semi and trailer parked just up the road. She grabs one of
the silver canisters and drives up to the Peter-Built. EMMA
closes her eyes and allows tears to run down her face.

The emergency flashers of the Peter-Built illuminate the
watery red eyes of EMMA. Two men are outside picking up the
canisters. Carla drives to the illuminated and heavily custom-
chromed red Semi and trailer. CARLA presses down her front
passenger side window where EMMA is sitting with her tearful
eyes still shut. Her tears are still running down her face.

                    JETHRO HOPPER
          Good evening! I saw your license
          plate. The name is Jethro Hopper,
          Mam. I hope I am not in too much
          trouble.

                    CARLA VIVIAN VAN HOLT-WILLIAMS
          No, not at all. I think this silver
          canister belongs to you. You've got
          several more back where I picked
          this one up.

JETHRO reaches in to grab the canister.

                    JETHRO HOPPER
          Thanks Mam.

EMMA slowly opens her eyes. She grabs the canister out of
CARLA'S hands while JETHRO still has his hands inside the
Dodge R/T Charger. EMMA presses her window up. JETHRO'S
wrist is trapped.

                    JETHRO HOPPER (CONT'D)
          You crazy lady? What's wrong with
          you?

                    CARLA VIVIAN VAN HOLT-WILLIAMS
          Let go honey! The canister belongs
          to Mr. Hopper.

                    JETHRO HOPPER
          Let the window down for God sake!

                    EMMA PETERSON
          No! Earl is inside, his head is in
          the canister. Don't take Earl from
          me.

                    CARLA VIVIAN VAN HOLT-WILLIAMS
Honey? Let it go. Just listen to
what you're saying!

                    JETHRO HOPPER
The window! The window! Damn it!
May I please have my hand back?

                    EMMA PETERSON
Earl is inside.

CARLA presses the down button on the passenger side window.

                    EMMA PETERSON (CONT'D)
Please just let me smell the inside
of the canister.

Tears flow down EMMA'S face.

                    EMMA PETERSON (CONT'D)
Please Agent Carla?

JETHRO reaches in and takes the canister out of CARLA'S hand.

                    JETHRO HOPPER
Boy oh boy! You're just out joy
riding with a transient, picking up
silver canisters along the roadside!

EMMA looks into the eyes of JETHRO. He can't believe it.
He's attracted to EMMA as he stares her in the face. But no
this can't be, *she's a transient*, he thinks to himself.

                    JETHRO HOPPER (CONT'D)
Who are you? Two FBI Agents
undercover?

                    EMMA PETERSON
Does the canister smell like death?

                    JETHRO HOPPER
What?

                    EMMA PETERSON
The canister! Sir, the canister
you're holding, does it smell like
death?

JETHRO smiles with a wide grin.

                    JETHRO HOPPER
"Smile...I'm on Candid Camera!" So
where are the cameras?
                    (MORE)

                    JETHRO HOPPER (CONT'D)
          Or is this Ridley's Believe it or
          Not? Cause, this sure ain't the
          Twilight Zone!

                    EMMA PETERSON
          Does the canister smell like death?

He mumbles under his breath his remark about EMMA'S state of
mind.

                    JETHRO HOPPER
          ...Stupid woman. Hey Wesley? Pass
          me a canister!

                    WESTLEY
          What?

                    JETHRO HOPPER
          Yeah just toss it! The one in your
          hand.

JETHRO tosses the canister to WESTLEY who just stands in
amazement wondering *"What the hell's going on"*? WESTLEY
tosses another canister and walks over to the Charger.

                    CARLA VIVIAN VAN HOLT-WILLIAMS
          Mr. Hopper sir? Would you please
          let this woman smell the inside of
          one of your canisters?

CARLA catches herself laughing at EMMA, so she regains her
composure. JETHRO hands EMMA another silver canister.

                    JETHRO HOPPER
          Here! Take a deep breath...take a
          whiff inside the canister first.

                    EMMA PETERSON
          No. No the other canister, let me
          smell the other one. Please!

JETHRO looks at WESTLEY. WESTLEY hands JETHRO the canister
he tossed to him. EMMA receives the one she asked for.

                    WESTLEY
          Jethro? What are you doing? We
          have work to do.

                    EMMA PETERSON
          Thank you sir.

She puts her face inside and inhales. With her head inside
the canister she begins to cry out loud.

She hands the canister back to JETHRO. CARLA steps on the gas.

> CARLA VIVIAN VAN HOLT-WILLIAMS
> Well? What did it smell like honey?

> EMMA PETERSON
> Si-si-silver!

EMMA leans back and rests her head on the head rest with tears still flowing down her face.

DISSOLVE TO:

64 **EXT. AGENT CARLA'S DODGE R/T CHARGER**   64

The Buffalo city line illuminates against the backdrop of stars and the moon. Agent Carla drives her triple black R/T on to the ramp of the highway that reads Downtown Buffalo.

> CARLA VIVIAN VAN HOLT-WILLIAMS
> It's sure pretty late. I'll take
> you home, but first I am taking you
> to FBI headquarters. Ok? Mrs.
> Peterson.

> EMMA PETERSON
> Don't call me that!

> CARLA VIVIAN VAN HOLT-WILLIAMS
> I am Carla Vivian Van Holt-williams,
> your friendly neighborhood FBI gal.

EMMA presses down her window and breathes the air of Buffalo.

> CARLA VIVIAN VAN HOLT-WILLIAMS (CONT'D)
> What? What did you say Mrs. Peterson?

> EMMA PETERSON
> I said don't call me that. Mrs.
> Peterson. That's not my name.

> CARLA VIVIAN VAN HOLT-WILLIAMS
> Unfortunately you are still indeed
> married to Jacob Peterson. Correct?

> EMMA PETERSON
> Not anymore. I am no longer his
> wife. I am getting a divorce. I am
> filing tomorrow.

> CARLA VIVIAN VAN HOLT-WILLIAMS
> I see.
> (MORE)

                    CARLA VIVIAN VAN HOLT-WILLIAMS (CONT'D)
          He cheated on you so you're leaving
          him. You're not going to kill him
          and stuff his head in a silver
          canister?

EMMA looks over at CARLA who smiles. Her nightmare was just
that. EMMA smiles back.

                    EMMA PETERSON
          I'm just leaving him. I'll get Earl
          to kill him.

                    CARLA VIVIAN VAN HOLT-WILLIAMS
          What? I have a habit of sometimes
          saying the wrong things at the wrong
          times. I apologize Emma.

                    EMMA PETERSON
          What would you do if you caught your
          husband cheating? You would stuff
          his head in a silver canister,
          wouldn't you Agent Van Holt-Williams?

                    CARLA VIVIAN VAN HOLT-WILLIAMS
          No Emma. I would just take out my
          pistol and shoot him in the head.
          We're almost at FBI headquarters.
          If you ever tell my superiors what I
          said, I'll deny it. Got that Emma?
          What's your maiden name?

                    EMMA PETERSON
          Cutler.

EMMA laughs at CARLA'S demeanor and poise.

                    EMMA PETERSON (CONT'D)
          Ever watch Dragnet or Spider-Man?
          Cause you're a riot Agent Carla Van
          Holt-Williams.

Her laughter continues. Amusing herself feels so good. She
finds herself healing from her laughter at CARLA'S expense.

                    EMMA PETERSON (CONT'D)
          You know it has been said that humor
          soothes and heals the soul. You've
          made me laugh. I feel much better
          now.

CARLA punches EMMA in the mouth. Emma takes her punch with
no problem. EMMA smiles a little.

                    EMMA PETERSON (CONT'D)
          You told me you were friendly.

EMMA fights to hold back her laughter. She can't help it.
Her soul needs to laugh, so she laughs.

               CARLA VIVIAN VAN HOLT-WILLIAMS
          Laugh on Emma! Emma, right?

                    EMMA PETERSON
          Yes, my name is Emma. Want my
          autograph? I don't have a pen.

EMMA smiles. CARLA frowns back...*What's wrong with this
woman?* EMMA laughs again. Agent VAN HOLT-WILLIAMS reminds
her of a *wanna-be* actress.

               CARLA VIVIAN VAN HOLT-WILLIAMS
          I'm a Van Holt. My great-great grand
          father was murdered at the hands of
          Earl Harold Paul back in 1899. My
          family has long ago moved out of the
          state of New York. Where is your
          family at? I mean do you have any
          brothers or sisters? Mom? Dad?
          Where do they live.

                    EMMA PETERSON
          My family is none of your business.
          You are a nut case Carla!

               CARLA VIVIAN VAN HOLT-WILLIAMS
          You want to learn how much of a nut
          case I am?

                    EMMA PETERSON
          I am in the presence of a Broadway
          star wanna be FBI Agent. What a
          wonderful actor you could become.
          Did you study acting?

CARLA slaps EMMA across the face. She's shocked but still
finds the Agent amusing.

                    EMMA PETERSON (CONT'D)
          Your badge! Let me see your badge.
          Agent Carla? We can roll play if
          you want. I love improvising.

CARLA slaps her twice more.

                    EMMA PETERSON (CONT'D)
          I pretend my three children were
          murdered by my ex-husband, I need
          desperately to find the head of my
          lover in a silver canister and you
          can pretend to play the part of the
          FBI Agent who'll capture my lover,
          the love of my life, Mr. Earl Harold
          Paul.

EMMA grabs CARLA'S weapon in her shoulder strap and cocks it
pressing the muzzle against her temple.

                    EMMA PETERSON (CONT'D)
          Let's call this scene *let-me-see-
          your-funky-stinkin-badge!*

CARLA punches EMMA in her mouth. EMMA doesn't flinch. She
pokes her in the temple a few more times with the muzzle of
CARLA'S own 9 millimeter pistol.

She has no intentions of insulting CARLA. EMMA begins to
laugh. The lost of her children is too much for her to bare.
EMMA realizes her laughter is soothing to her soul.

                    CARLA VIVIAN VAN HOLT-WILLIAMS
          Don't laugh at me.

                    EMMA PETERSON
          I am not laughing at you.

CARLA takes her badge from around her neck. She hands it to
EMMA. EMMA enjoys poking CARLA in her temple as she is
looking at her badge. CARLA with both hands on the wheel,
is stunned. How could she have let this happen.

                    CARLA VIVIAN VAN HOLT-WILLIAMS
          Give me back my weapon!

EMMA pulls the trigger! The pistol fires. *Empty.* The 9mm
is empty to EMMA'S surprise. CARLA'S life flashes before
her. She forgot to load her weapon.

                    CARLA VIVIAN VAN HOLT-WILLIAMS (CONT'D)
          Don't worry I will not arrest you.
          Just give me back my pistol!

CARLA mumbles.

                    CARLA VIVIAN VAN HOLT-WILLIAMS (CONT'D)
          You were laughing at me. I hate it
          when people laugh at me!

                    EMMA PETERSON
          You hate it when people don't believe
          you're a real FBI Agent...except
          well for today, you hate it when you
          forget to load your weapon. I'm not
          too fond of being punched or slapped.
          I've got to get some rest before I
          lose my mind. Here's your pistol
          Agent Carla.

EMMA pokes CARLA a few more times. She takes her weapon
from EMMA and places it back in her holster. EMMA pulls
down the sun visor. The light illuminates her face. She
fixes her hair trying to remove all the dirt.

                    EMMA PETERSON (CONT'D)
          Ok! So aren't you FBI Agents trained
          to keep your gun loaded at all
          times...especially when you're at
          work?

EMMA licks the blood from her bottom lip as she tosses CARLA'S
badge into her lap. CARLA pulls into the driveway parking
structure of the FBI building. Emma continues to suck her
lower lip. CARLA is still stunned she's not dead.

65 INT. FBI HEADQUARTERS PARKING STRUCTURE -- CONTINUOUS 65

CARLA drives her Dodge R/T Charger into her reserved parking
space. Her license reads: US GOVERNMENT VAN HOLT.

                    CARLA VIVIAN VAN HOLT-WILLIAMS (V.O.)
          Yeah! My weapon is suppose to be
          loaded at all times, Mrs.-

                    EMMA PETERSON (V.O.)
          Don't. Don't you dare.

                    CARLA VIVIAN VAN HOLT-WILLIAMS (V.O.)
          I won't say it. I'll call you Emma.
          Emma Cutler. You'll be home shortly.

                    EMMA PETERSON (V.O.)
          That's all I want and a hot bubble
          bath.

                    CARLA VIVIAN VAN HOLT-WILLIAMS (V.O.)
          You want some black coffee?

                    EMMA PETERSON (V.O.)
          No, then I'll never go to sleep.

CARLA VIVIAN VAN HOLT-WILLIAMS (V.O.)
Ok then.

FADE OUT:

FADE IN:

66 EXT. FBI HEADQUARTERS INTERROGATION ROOM -- NIGHT   66

FBI Agents and Buffalo Police have Jacob Peterson in chains
in an orange jump prison suit with a picture of his family
posted on an easel display with the words MURDERED underneath.
They listen to the chant of EARL and his family members.
Then video footage of EARL and his employees at the EHP Waste
Management Plant are seen casting their victims alive into
the incinerators. The FBI footage is played on DVD and showed
on a personal laptop.

While EARL and his employees are seen chanting while
committing their crimes of genocide, Agents ROGER MICKEY
MADISON, NIGEL OSCAR KNOLL, FELIX FRANKLIN HAYES, and Police
Detectives, ANITA CRUZ, LAWRENCE WILLIAMS, LT. JACQUELINE
JENKINS are asking questions of EMMA simultaneously.

Several easels display pictures of EARL, his family members
and members of his company.

Photographs of Professor JEREMIAH PETERSON and MAPLE MARY
taken in 1899 are also displayed. A black hand drawn picture
of what an illustrator interprets AMMONOTHUS the WRAITH MAN
to look like is pinned next to a picture of EARL. Underneath
the illustration portrait is the question "Do you Believe..."

The digital audio recording is played twice more with the
volume turned down low.

EARL & FAMILY (V.O.)
Adulterers you'll die die die! Your
stinkin' rotten tongues are filled
with lies. Cut cut cut, I'll cut
your tongue! So you won't taste,
taste taste taste the sweet ravishing
flavor of other men's wives.

CARLA VIVIAN VAN HOLT-WILLIAMS
You're tired. I know, Emma.

JACOB PETERSON is in another room at a table in an orange
jump suit with sheriffs standing in the corner of the room.
EMMA can see him on a television monitor. She looks up at
the screen with hate in her eyes. Every word that he speaks
EMMA can hear and he knows that he is being seen by her. He
stares into the camera.

He can hear what is being said by EMMA and the other law
enforcement seated at a table with her.

> JACOB PETERSON
> It wasn't me Emma. The Ammonothus,
> the Wraith Man made me kill our
> children. I told you he made me do
> it! He made me do it...Oh yes he
> did!

NIGEL flashes his FBI Badge in front of EMMA.

> NIGEL OSCAR KNOLL
> My name is Knoll. Agent Nigel Oscar
> Knoll. Does the name Professor
> Jeremiah Peterson mean anything to
> you?

> JACOB PETERSON
> How could you let the devil sleep
> with you Emma? How could you let
> Earl touch you? I know he touched
> you. I know you slept with the
> devil...Oh yes you did!

EMMA sheds a tear and remains silent.

> ROGER MICKEY MADISON
> Earl Harold Paul has been the center
> of mysterious murders ever since my
> great great grand mother Maple Mary
> slept with Professor Jeremiah Peterson
> back in 1899. My name is Agent Roger
> Mickey Madison.

EMMA gives a half-smile.

> JACOB PETERSON
> Wake up out of your Earl Harold Paul
> wonderland, Emma!

There's a tremor. The building shakes. The lights flicker.
A voice over the intercom speaks.

> FBI AGENT (V.O.)
> Stay calm. We're checking it out.

> LAWRENCE WILLIAMS
> Emma, I am Detective Lawrence
> Williams. I work for the Buffalo
> Police Department and this is my
> partner Detective Anita Cruz.

EMMA PETERSON
She's your lover. Adulterer!

ANITA CRUZ
Hello, Emma. Your lover is Earl
Harold Paul. Where is he?

EMMA PETERSON
I don't know where my future husband
is. Earl is coming for me I can
feel his presence. He's coming to
rescue me.

ANITA CRUZ
We know you're not a murderer. We
just need to know the last time you
were with him.

JACQUELINE JENKINS
You were with him at a Seafood
establishment? I'm Lieutenant
Jacqueline Jenkins.

JACOB PETERSON
She was not only with him...He made
you cum didn't he Emma? His seed is
growing inside of you now! I want a
divorce...Oh yes I do!

EMMA PETERSON
Not a problem. Earl will be my new
husband. We will have children and
we will raise a family to wipe out
all of the Adulterers!

ANITA CRUZ
Why do you want a dead man, cause
I'll kill him before you wed him.
Prisoners get married all the time.
You'll be married to a corpse.

JACQUELINE JENKINS
I'll have Detectives Williams and
Cruz drive you home.

EMMA PETERSON
That wouldn't be a good idea.

CARLA VIVIAN VAN HOLT-WILLIAMS
Why? Ms. Cutler. Cutler is her
maiden name.

                    EMMA PETERSON
          I hate adulterers. So does Earl.
          Jacob? I'll have the divorce papers
          sent to your cell. You should have
          them by the end of the week...or
          should I lay them on your grave? By
          the morning you'll be dead.

                    JACOB PETERSON
          I want protection. Ammonothus the
          Wraith Man and Earl Harold Paul are
          both coming to kill me and all of
          the Adulterers in this building. I
          want protection. I have rights!
          I'm insane! Ammonothus the Wraith
          Man made me do it. He made me do
          it. Oh yes...He did!

JACOB yells as if some invisible force or demon in is mind
is speaking to him saying...*Oh no he did not. You're
lying...You're lying I tell you!*

                    JACOB PETERSON (CONT'D)
          Yes he did! Yes he did! My hand
          was f-f-for...*forced!* My hand was
          forced to pick up my gun and shoot
          my family and my lover. I morn for
          Judith Edith! I morn for the lost
          of my three children!

Please believe my words! He thinks within himself.

                    JACOB PETERSON (CONT'D)
          Why...would I lie?

JACOB weeps.

                    JACOB PETERSON (CONT'D)
          I have no reason. Not a single one.
          My soul is in trouble! Ammonothus
          the Wraith Man is coming for me and
          his wicked wretched immortal servant
          Earl Harold Paul.

EMMA yells.

                    EMMA PETERSON
          You leave my future husband out of
          this...you *sick-freak* of nature!
          Adulterer! Adulterer! *Die die die!*
          By the *Finger of God* you will die.

                    CARLA VIVIAN VAN HOLT-WILLIAMS
...Emma? Just tell us the last time
you were with Earl, then I'll take
you home.

                    EMMA PETERSON
The last time I was with him I was
riding in his limo and we both shared
the greatest orgasms of our lives!
Then we were in the Seafood Palace.
That is when I saw the Applegate
News flash. That's when I first
learned of the death's of my Billy,
Samantha and Lisa. My children.
You murdered my children!

                    CARLA VIVIAN VAN HOLT-WILLIAMS
I'll take Emma Cutler home now.

                    FELIX FRANKLIN HAYES
Just one moment. I'm Agent Felix
Franklin Hayes. Do you believe in
visions and dreams?

                    JACOB PETERSON
I do!

His words are ignored.

                    EMMA PETERSON
I dream.

                    FELIX FRANKLIN HAYES
Do have them regularly? Have you
ever dreamt of a 16ft. man?

                    EMMA PETERSON
Yes Agent Hayes. When I was a little
girl I met the Moth Man on a camping
trip in the hills of West Virginia.
I asked him how tall he was and he
told me he was twenty feet tall.
May I go home now?

There is a tremor and the building shakes again.

                    FBI AGENT (V.O.)
Everyone stay calm.

                    FELIX FRANKLIN HAYES
Have you ever seen Ammonothus the
Wraith Man?

                    ROGER MICKEY MADISON
          You saw him didn't you?

                    NIGEL OSCAR KNOLL
          How tall was he? Sixteen feet? Did
          you see the Nephilim, written about
          in the book of Enoch and recorded in
          Genesis the first book of Moses?

                    JACQUELINE JENKINS
          You guys aren't just your ordinary
          FBI Agents? I think we can let Emma
          go home.

The lights continue to flicker.

                    JACQUELINE JENKINS (CONT'D)
          What's wrong with this building?

                    CARLA VIVIAN VAN HOLT-WILLIAMS
          When it rained placentas and seven-
          month old unborn children ripped
          open their sacks they were illuminated
          and walked toward you. You talked
          to them.

                    FELIX FRANKLIN HAYES
          We have witnesses that say they saw
          you talking to unborn babies.

                    EMMA PETERSON
          You knew? All this time you knew?

Suddenly, as EMMA looks at the ceiling, she notices a large
seven-month old placenta, like a wasp nest, on the ceiling.

She looks around at the detectives and agents. All eyes are
on her. Only she sees the placenta as it falls on to the
table. EMMA is the only one experiencing this vision. The
seven-month old baby boy rips open the bag. He is bloody
and his fluids begin to slowly fill the table.

He walks closer to Emma.

                    LITTLE BOO BOO
          Ma-ma. Daddy loves me. You love
          me. He wanted me to tell you hello.

Emma's eyes are full of tears.

                    EMMA PETERSON
          Yes. I love you.

                    LITTLE BOO BOO
          Guess what? Daddy is inside!

LITTLE BOO BOO points to the placenta. EMMA cannot believe
what she is experiencing. She is frightened but glad to see
the child she realizes is hers. Everyone in the room is
suddenly looking at EMMA talking to herself.

                    EMMA PETERSON
          Where's Daddy? Show me where daddy
          is ok? Little Boo Boo. Go get daddy.

LITTLE BOO BOO walks over to the sticky placenta. It is
sticking to LITTLE BOO BOO'S hands so he wipes the fluids on
his legs then opens the placenta and sticks his head inside.

The people in the room continue to stare at EMMA. The FBI
Agents don't see anything that is happening to EMMA. They
whisper amongst themselves because they believe in
phenomenons.

                    ROGER MICKEY MADISON
          We're going to have to take Emma to
          Area 51. After we catch Earl Harold
          Paul.

                    CARLA VIVIAN VAN HOLT-WILLIAMS
          She's going through a phenomenon! I
          just know it.

                    ROGER MICKEY MADISON
          We have to get Emma out of here!

                    NIGEL OSCAR KNOLL
          I'll go get the helicopter ready!

                    FELIX FRANKLIN HAYES
          Ammonothus the Wraith Man is on the
          top of the roof. I can sense it.

                    JACQUELINE JENKINS
          Ok what's going on? Hey? What are
          you all mumbling about?

67 <u>**INT. LITTLE BOO BOO'S PLACENTA**</u> **-- MOMENTS LATER**   **67**

He looks around in the fluids. Then he sees his father.
LITTLE BOO BOO gives his daddy a big smile.

EARL whispers.

                    EARL HAROLD PAUL
          Tell your mommy I said to close her
          eyes and keep them closed.

> LITTLE BOO BOO
> Ok daddy. Love you.

> EARL HAROLD PAUL
> I love you too Little Boo Boo!

68 EXT. FBI HEADQUARTERS INTERROGATION ROOM -- CONTINUOUS 68

The police are perplexed. Agent CARLA tries to get EMMA up from her chair but she refuses and keeps looking at LITTLE BOO BOO who places his finger over his mouth. Still no one sees what EMMA is experiencing.

> LITTLE BOO BOO
> Where are you going Ma-ma?

> EMMA PETERSON
> No where Little Boo Boo. Where's Daddy?

> LITTLE BOO BOO
> Daddy says to close your eyes and keep them closed. Don't open your eyes. Ok Mommy? No peaking!

> EMMA PETERSON
> Ok ok. Little Boo Boo. Mommy is closing her eyes.

EMMA begins to weep.

> EMMA PETERSON (CONT'D)
> But I want to see Daddy. I love him so much. I love you too.

> LITTLE BOO BOO
> Keep them closed. Here comes Daddy!

EMMA reluctantly closes her eyes while slapping away the hands of Agent CARLA. Suddenly, everyone in the room sees the placenta. LITTLE BOO BOO and EARL come out covered in fluids. He is as tall as LITTLE BOO BOO. EARL stands beside their son gazing into EMMA'S eyes.

> EARL HAROLD PAUL
> My Dearest Emma. You will make a wonderful mother for our son.

EARL gets down on one knee soaked in fluids.

> EARL HAROLD PAUL (CONT'D)
> Will you marry me?

                    EMMA PETERSON
          Oh Earl!

EARL sees JACOB in the television monitor. JACOB sees EARL.

                  EARL HAROLD PAUL
          Hold your answer for later. No
          peaking my delicious sweetness.

The officers are stunned as they watch EARL jump through the
television monitor. Lt JENKINS covers her mouth. She is
afraid while her detectives draw their weapons. The Agents
try to prevent them from shooting by grabbing their arms,
but EARL is on the other side, where the sheriffs fire upon
EARL.

                    JACOB PETERSON
          Get me out of here! He's going to
          kill me.

EARL bullets go into his chest as he jumps on to the table.
JACOB is handcuffed to his chair. EARL causes the bullets
to move from his chest into his mouth. He spits out the
bullets killing the two sheriffs.

The building shakes due to a tremor.

                    FBI AGENT (V.O.)
          Evacuate! Evacuate! FBI
          headquarters. Immediately.
          Ammonothus the Wraith Man is on the
          roof. All personnel evacuate
          immediately!

Alarms are heard and officers run down the halls pass the
interrogation rooms.

EARL jumps on JACOB'S chest, as the building begins to
crumble. The ceiling begins to cave in.

                    EMMA PETERSON
          Ok Earl I am going to open my eyes.
          I want to see you!

EARL takes his knife and slits JACOB'S throat. He assaults
JACOB repeatedly stabbing him in his chest.

                  EARL HAROLD PAUL
          Die! Descendant of Professor Jeremiah
          Peterson! Adulterer die die die!

EARL HAROLD PAUL looks at LITTLE BOO BOO who is watching
him. The blood pours out of JACOB'S throat. EARL begins
pulling the tongue out of JACOB'S mouth.

Then he stops while holding JACOB'S tongue his face looks
surprised as he sees his son smiling with a devilish grin.

                    EARL HAROLD PAUL (CONT'D)
          Get back inside Little Boo Boo!

EMMA opens her eyes and sees the miniature EARL, in the
television monitor standing twelve inches tall upon the chest
of her estranged husband. She begins to smile!

MR. PAUL jumps into the air swinging around JACOB'S head to
the back side of his neck. He brings his knife high above
his head and stabs him in the back of his skull. LITTLE BOO
BOO is stunned then he begins to grin as he climbs back into
the placenta.

Suddenly, EARL passes through the television with lightning
speed and jumps inside the placenta. The he peaks his head
out and looks at Detective Williams.

                    EARL HAROLD PAUL (CONT'D)
          You're next Adulterer! You are next
          to die die die!

Lawrence tries to shoot but ROGER prevents him. The
Detectives and Agents look at EMMA who continues to smile
down at the placenta with a devilish grin. Then she realizes
she is being watched. She looks up at them all. When she
looks into the eyes of CARLA she faints into her arms.

                    JACQUELINE JENKINS
          Die you murdering bastard!

JACQUELINE aims her gun at the placenta and fires. EARL
coughs up blood as he lifts the placenta over his head hiding
inside. The placenta begins to deflate in a mist of vapor.
Then the placenta stops deflating. It is now a blob of sticky
lumpy liquid. The Agents open their briefcases put gloves
on and begin putting what is left of the placenta into tube
containers.

ANITA CRUZ helps CARLA with EMMA as they both walk over to
the door. CARLA looks into her husband eyes.

                    CARLA VIVIAN VAN HOLT-WILLIAMS
          You've been cheating on me with her.

                    ANITA CRUZ
          So what! He's my man now.

                    CARLA VIVIAN VAN HOLT-WILLIAMS
          He's my husband!

                    ANITA CRUZ
          I have been your husband's joy for
          over a year.

               CARLA VIVIAN VAN HOLT-WILLIAMS
          Anita has been your whore for over a
          year?

                    ANITA CRUZ
          Let's not do this. What will your
          fellow agents think of you if I kick
          your ass right now?

                  JACQUELINE JENKINS
          Not now! Anita take Emma to her
          home and wait there until I find out
          what the hell just happen.

She mumbles to herself.

               JACQUELINE JENKINS (CONT'D)
          What the...the hell just happen?

                ROGER MICKEY MADISON
          You along with us, just witnessed a
          phenomenon! You're right. We have
          to get Emma to a safe place. Carla,
          I want you to take Emma to her house
          and get her belongings.

                  JACQUELINE JENKINS
          What?

                ROGER MICKEY MADISON
          We are taking her to Area 51.

                FELIX FRANKLIN HAYES
          Emma will be safe there.

                 NIGEL OSCAR KNOLL
          We'll need to run some tests.

                  JACQUELINE JENKINS
          Anita? Go with Carla. No fighting
          ladies.

The building stops shaking and the lights stop flickering.

               JACQUELINE JENKINS (CONT'D)
          Lets get out of this building.

                ROGER MICKEY MADISON
          Sounds good to me.

                    JACQUELINE JENKINS
Agent Madison? Just one thing.
Does the government have an ET?
Just always wanted to know.

                    LAWRENCE WILLIAMS
Lieutenant, don't you listen to *AM
Talk Radio* at midnight? My
grandfather and I always did before
he passed on in the gray celestial
clouds.

                    ANITA CRUZ
God rest your grandfather's soul.

                    LAWRENCE WILLIAMS
God rest his sweet soul. They not
only have an ET, they've got King
Kong and Godzilla.

Over the top and melodramatic, Anita Cruz whispers.

                    ANITA CRUZ
The FEDS? They also have the Hulk,
Big Foot and the Moth Man somewhere
deep underground. Within the
labyrinth of tunnels at Area 51.

                    JACQUELINE JENKINS
But that is all top secret!

                    ROGER&NIGEL&FELIX&CARLA
Affirmative Lieutenant! That is all
top secret. Very top secret!

                    ANITA CRUZ
That is why when you are away on
your many top secret missions, I
fulfill all of your husband's needs.

                                        FADE TO BLACK:

The sound of ANITA'S face being punched fills our ears.

                    ANITA CRUZ (V.O.) (CONT'D)
Ouch! I deserved that.

                    EMMA PETERSON (V.O.)
Where's my man? Let go of me. Let
go! I can smell his scent of death
all around me. Let me go to him.
He needs me. Where are you Earl
Harold Paul? Where are you?

FADE IN:

69 <u>EXT. FBI HEADQUARTERS</u> -- NIGHT   69

The moon is brightly shining. The clouds roll across the
October sky by the winds in downtown Buffalo. Agent NIGEL
OSCAR KNOLL is circling, hovering high above the FBI
headquarters in a black helicopter. AMMONOTHUS THE WRAITH
MAN, stands on the roof making the building sway back and
forth. Four police helicopters turn on their search lights.
Applegate News helicopter hover over the FBI Building and
streets below.

SWAT teams are in the nearby windows across the street from
the FBI Building. They are also on the rooftops aiming their
weapons at Ammonothus. Lt Jenkins, Detectives ANITA CRUZ
and LAWRENCE WILLIAMS are accompanied by other officers as
Agent CARLA escorts EMMA to her R/T Charger. ANITA CRUZ
assists CARLA with EMMA, who looks upwards towards the rooftop
of the FBI Building trying to get a glimpse of Ammonothus.

Several black FBI Chevy Yukons with tinted glass are parked
outside the headquarters. FBI Agents stand by the Yukons.

More police vehicles begin rolling down the street setting
up their perimeters around the FBI headquarters. Four Police
Crown Victorias pull up to the headquarters. Lt. JENKINS
gives instructions to the detectives, when they all notice
AMMONOTHUS on the roof top.

AMMONOTHUS soars in the clouds looking for EARL. The search
lights in the street below are on him as he dives to the
street below.

ROGER MICKEY MADISON is being escorted by FELIX FRANKLIN
HAYES. ROGER holds the container with the partially liquid
and lumpy placenta bag inside as he walks out the double
doors of the FBI Building.

A red mist begins to escape the container. The Agents do
not notice the red vapor.

AMMONOTHUS THE WRAITH MAN ascends upon the Buffalo detectives
and police officers and FBI agents as they fire their weapons.

Police officers are thrown to the sides of their cars as
they try to subdue the sixteen foot AMMONOTHUS.

From behind him the SWAT Team tackles AMMONOTHUS, but he
disappears ripping their heads off their necks in his arms.

Their headless bodies fall to their knees then to the ground
with blood pouring out at the feet of AMMONOTHUS. Their
bodies keep moving toward him.

Their hands grab a hold of his legs and ankles.

AMMONOTHUS reappears clinging to the side of the FBI Building
with his hands like a spider. The headless officers let go
of his legs landing on the pavement. In his sleeves are the
heads of the unfortunate officers whose bodies still have
life in them lying on the ground below.

FBI Agents below open fire. On the rooftops across the street
SWAT officers open fire. Windows of the FBI Building shatter.
AMMONOTHUS sees the container in the arms of Agent MADISON.
He sees in the red mist the 12inch tall ghostly figure of
EARL HAROLD PAUL trapped inside.

EARL coughs up blood. He looks up at AMMONOTHUS clinging
the building.

                    EARL HAROLD PAUL
          Help me Ammonothus! Save me my Wraith
          Master.

AMMONOTHUS causes the heads to roll into his hands from inside
his sleeves. He blows fire out of his mouth igniting them
on fire. He throws the burning skulls into the crowd of law
enforcement officers below.

The flaming skulls crash into the window shields of police
cars. The vehicles explode.

Buffalo Police jump AMMONOTHUS with night sticks as he hovers
down from the building in the middle of the street.

AMMONOTHUS takes four night sticks from the officers. Holding
two in each hand he begins to assault the officers with their
own sticks.

Suddenly, there is thunder in the heavens. A dance of
lightning over downtown Buffalo races through the skyline.

AMMONOTHUS looks up in the clouds and is frightened at the
sight of ghostly images of Sister VICTORIA CONNIE YORK-
BAINBRIDGE and her husband Reverend THOMAS HENRY. He is
frighten as he sees THOMAS and VICTORIA twirl their *Whips
of Righteousness"* in the air over their heads.

The Buffalo SWAT Team fires its rounds from on top of the
near by buildings and from inside of the widows.

AMMONOTHUS is preoccupied with his vision of the Reverend
and his wife in the heavens as he sees them smile down from
the moon lit sky. His head is being torn a part by the
rounds.

Suddenly, his head is miraculously healed. As he continues to gaze into the sky his vision slowly vanishes in the rays of the moonlight.

The rounds of the officers weapons are lodged inside of his skull and face.

AMMONOTHUS takes a deep breath through his nose and spits out the rounds through his mouth at the SWAT Team in the windows across the street.

The SWAT officers fall to their death.

A FBI helicopter lands in the street near the headquarters building. Agents ROGER and FELIX board the helicopter with the container. EARL is still trapped inside and he stands proudly 12inches high covered in placenta fluids.

The FBI helicopter ascends into the illuminated city skyline below the clouds that are filled with colorful electrical energy.

AMMONOTHUS soars into the air after the helicopter with five Buffalo Police officers hanging on to him.

Agent NIGEL OSCAR KNOLL pilots his helicopter. He nearly collides with Captain HOWARD and reporter APPLEGATE who hovered by in their APPLEGATE NEWS helicopter.

EARL HAROLD PAUL, still trapped inside, begins to cough up more blood as he beats his fist against the container. His knife is not sharp enough to penetrate the container he finds himself imprisoned.

Dark green EHP Waste Management trucks roll down the street in front of the FBI headquarters crashing into the Police and FBI vehicles.

EARL'S MEN begin to fight the police with knives in their hands slashing their throats.

Lightning and colorful displays of light fill the clouds as thunder rolls in the atmosphere above the downtown city line.

In the Dodge R/T Charger EMMA tries to free herself from the back seat while detective ANITA CRUZ riding beside her restrains her in her seat with her arms and hands.

AMMONOTHUS becomes invisible but only one officer falls to his death as he continues to free fall above the city line over downtown.

Fans of AMMONOTHUS THE WRAITH MAN cheer as search lights on top of the buildings follow him as he is carried by the wind.

He reaches the FBI helicopter.

Agent CARLA sees the body of the officer falling towards her wind shield. She puts the R/T Charger in reverse and steps on the gas.

The R/T's wheels spin gripping the asphalt.

The officer lands face forward on to the pavement missing CARLA'S car.

AMMONOTHUS grabs the container which opens.

EARL HAROLD PAUL escapes jumping out of the helicopter free falling into the wind. He grows to his life like size.

Reporter APPLEGATE reports the breaking news as it happens.

70 **INT. APPLEGATE NEWS HELICOPTER** -- CONTINUOUS   **70**

The Applegate News helicopter dives into the direction of EARL but nearly collides into the FBI helicopter navigated by Agent NIGEL.

> AGNES ANNA APPLEGATE
> Look Captain Howard! Look why don't
> you? There's Mr. Earl Harold Paul
> free falling to his death!

> CAPTAIN HOWARD
> I see Agnes. I see!

The FBI helicopter pulls up while Applegate helicopter continues to trail EARL. The FBI helicopter begins to dive ahead of the Applegate helicopter.

> AGNES ANNA APPLEGATE
> Watch! Watch where you fly! My
> father and his father and his father
> entrusted me with every piece of
> equipment belonging to the Applegate
> News Paper Corporation and Television
> Studios before they died. I don't
> wish to meet anyone of them today!
> Understand Captain Howard?

71 **EXT. FBI HELICOPTER**-- CONTINUOUS   **71**

Nigel dives to prevent AMMONOTHUS from coming aboard. Agent ROGER draws his pistol into the hideous face of AMMONOTHUS.

> CAPTAIN HOWARD (V.O.)
> Agnes Anna Applegate?
> (MORE)

                    CAPTAIN HOWARD (V.O.) (CONT'D)
          That's why I'm the Captain and you're
          n'... Just let me do my job?

AMMONOTHUS free falls from the FBI helicopter and catches
EARL HAROLD PAUL as the Applegate News helicopter dives
following behind.

72 <u>**FULL SHOT CLOUDS**</u> -- **CONTINUOUS**   **72**

The moon light and the stars shine down on the electrical
movement of lightning in the clouds over the city line of
Buffalo.

                    AGNES ANNA APPLEGATE (V.O.)
          Aye! Aye! Captain.

                    CAPTAIN HOWARD (V.O.)
          I can do without the Aye Aye! Just
          let me do what you pay me to do.

                    AGNES ANNA APPLEGATE (V.O.)
          Ok.

The three officers hold on to AMMONOTHUS as he soars higher
into the sky above the clouds into the moon light.

While in the arms of his Wraith Master, EARL HAROLD PAUL
sees DARLENE BAINBRIDGE. DARLENE stares back with tears in
her eyes.

AMMONOTHUS is frightened at the sight of the Angelic Beings
surrounding DARLENE. He dives to the street below towards
the FBI Building. Following behind is the FBI and Applegate
News helicopters. DARLENE watches as they follow AMMONOTHUS
to the city below.

AMMONOTHUS looks back. He sees the illuminated *"Whip of
Righteousness"* being whirled around in the air by DARLENE'S
parents. The very ends of the Whip is as long as a football
field which is a blazing consuming fire that never burns
out. Their ghostly images seem to be made of light. DARLENE
and her parents are as bright as the moon. The ANGELIC BEINGS
that surround them are dressed in blue and purple robes.
Their eyes are on fire and do not look human but appear to
be diamonds. Diamonds consumed in flames.

                                        DISSOLVE TO:

73 <u>**EXT. FBI HEADQUARTERS**</u> -- **MOMENTS LATER**   **73**

Coming down out of the sky here he comes! AMMONOTHUS THE
WRAITH MAN!

The diabolic villain and his human servant EARL HAROLD PAUL an immortal man of death and destruction, believing himself to be the *finger of God*.

He hovers on the currents of the wind to the street as the other officers fall to their knees and look up into the dance of blue, green, red and white lightning in the sky.

The three officers fall to their knees, their mouths wide open. They can hardly believe what they just saw.

The crowd of citizens stand on the side walk looking up into the heavens in wonder with their mouths wide open.

The law enforcement keeps the crowd from coming into the street while others hold their weapons cocking them and begin to open fire on AMMONOTHUS and EARL HAROLD PAUL.

AMMONOTHUS blows fire out of his mouth. The officers who were on their knees still gazing into the heavens are now consumed in flames. He protects EARL who hides behind him.

The three kneeling officers begin to lift their hands. Their illuminated spirits leave their bodies and soar up into the heavens.

Suddenly, there is a great BOOM! In the heavens. Their spirits leave their bodies and ascend up into the clouds. Thunder rolls once more into the atmosphere while the sky reflects the continued dance of electrical energy.

The officers are overcome by the EHP Waste Management-men in dark green jumpsuits fighting them in the street.

AMMONOTHUS holds EARL in his arms, shielding him from the bullets. He coughs up blood. EARL smiles. His tears run down his face then suddenly escape defying gravity. EARL tries to stand to his feet on his own without his Wraith Master's help.

The street fighting is once again subdued by Police as Agents surround AMMONOTHUS and EARL HAROLD PAUL.

AMMONOTHUS stares into he eyes of the FBI agents.

                    AMMONOTHUS
          Leave me and my servant alone. Leave,
          leave us alone! Put your arms around
          my waist Earl Harold Paul and let my
          anointing of iniquity give you
          strength. Feel the absence of Peace
          within my soul. Let my spirit, the
          scent and power of death flow through
          you!

The Agents draw their weapons as AMMONOTHUS yells out his unearthly howling cry to try to scare them into submission to his command. AMMONOTHUS looks frightened as he looks once more into the sky.

The Agents fire their weapons. The BULLETS race with great speed out of their chambers.

AMMONOTHUS takes a deep breath and opens his mouth, and with all of this might, as his lungs cause his chest to expand abnormally.

He exhales. Blue, orange and white flames come forth out of this mouth.

The BULLETS begin to melt slowly, ever so slowly. The bullets lose their velocity in the flames from his mouth. The rounds evaporate in the intense heat of the fire.

The flames over take the path of the BULLETS and set the Agents on fire. While standing their spirits escape their bodies and soar into the clouds.

Buffalo's finest Detective Lawrence Williams walks between the Agents on fire. He holds his weapon in the face of AMMONOTHUS who looks down towering over him.

LAWRENCE notices EARL hiding behind him. Other Police Officers stand behind LAWRENCE as the three Agents' bodies begin burning into ashes.

EARL stands proudly. His supporters in the crowd begin to cheer. He has regained his strength. He wipes his mouth of blood. He spits saliva out of his mouth. He moves AMMONOTHUS out of his way. The Wraith Master stands behind his servant.

> EARL HAROLD PAUL
> These men belong to me. You are all
> adulterers and I am the finger of
> God! I am. I am. I am the finger
> of God!

> EARL'S SUPPORTERS
> He is! He is! He is the finger of
> God!

Suddenly, EARL raises his knife to the eye level of LAWRENCE and his boss LT. JACQUELINE JENKINS. She walks up beside him, she notices from the heavens above the two illuminated *Whips of Righteousness* consuming in flames descend upon AMMONOTHUS.

The *Whips of Righteousness* grab him by his waist and he is pulled into the heavens above downtown Buffalo.

EARL looks up. His supporters continue to chant.

More electrical energy in the sky illuminates the rolling clouds in the moon lit night.

Police fire their weapons into the chest of EARL. Foolishly LAWRENCE grabs the back of EARL'S neck and cuts his throat.

The officers hold their fire. Blood pours out of the neck of the IMMORTAL MAN. The crowd's chanting dies.

EARL grabs LAWRENCE'S throat and squeezes.

EARL'S neck begins to heal.

> EARL HAROLD PAUL
> You can't kill me. I'm already dead.
> I am immortal. Didn't know?

> LAWRENCE WILLIAMS
> Well I'm not. You're under arrest...

LAWRENCE recites the *Miranda Rights* to EARL.

74 EXT. DODGE R/T CHARGER -- CONTINUOUS   74

Agent CARLA drives her R/T Charger towards MR. PAUL.

> CARLA VIVIAN VAN HOLT-WILLIAMS
> Kill him Earl Harold Paul!

> ANITA CRUZ
> What? What are you doing!

> CARLA VIVIAN VAN HOLT-WILLIAMS
> Kill the Adulterer!

> EMMA PETERSON
> Earl? Earl! Save your sweetness!
> Rescue me Earl!

Agent CARLA slams on the brakes as she sees a bright light illuminating the sky for a moment. Then the light quickly fades away as AMMONOTHUS descends from the sky out of the fading colorful array of electrical energy.

He grabs both EARL and LAWRENCE in his arms. AMMONOTHUS ascends into the clouds still entangled in the illuminated fiery *Whips of Righteousness*.

AMMONOTHUS disappears into the clouds above.

CARLA puts her car in reverse while watching the sky.

The head of the detective tumbles down out of the sky with his body following behind. His body falls to the street. His head bounces on to the roof as CARLA steps on the gas.

CARLA drives away through the crowd as officers handcuff the supporters of the IMMORTAL MAN. She drives through the city to the nearby highway as the clouds over the city line dance again with their colorful display of light.

75 **FULL SHOT CLOUDS OVER DOWNTOWN BUFFALO (MINIATURE)** --
MOMENTS LATER

Agent CARLA'S R/T Charger travels down the highway below with cop cars trailing. Above the city line in the moonlight the spirit of Reverend THOMAS HENRY BAINBRIDGE and his wife Sister VICTORIA CONNIE YORK-BAINBRIDGE take AMMONOTHUS to the top Buffalo Cathedral of Mercy inside its Bell Tower.

EARL faints into the arms of DARLENE BAINBRIDGE. She lays him down in her lap as she sits in the clouds. EARL'S eyes are closed. Her beauty is radiant in the moon light of this night. Her voice is soothing her childhood friend. He smiles a little.

> DARLENE BAINBRIDGE
> My parents took your Wraith Master
> inside the bell tower of their former
> church, the Buffalo Methodist
> Cathedral of Mercy. Inside the tower
> he will receive his punishment by
> the *Whips of Righteousness*.

DARLENE looks down at the Methodist Cathedral in the distance. She witnesses her parents punish AMMONOTHUS THE WRAITH MAN. The cloud she sits on travels to the Cathedral below. The church is near Niagara Falls Park and its famous river.

> REV.THOMAS HENRY BAINBRIDGE
> Principality. Powers and Might your
> under my feet in this shining
> moonlight. Ammonothus. Ammonothus.
> For destroying Earl's mind, take and
> feel every lash from this whip, made
> from the Living Vine...

> SIS. VICTORIA CONNIE YORK-BAINBRIDGE
> ...Spiritual Wickedness Ruler on
> high, Wraith of Darkness, receive
> your whipping, in agony in agony in
> agony tonight!

AMMONOTHUS lays prostrate across the Bell of the Cathedral. He howls his horrid cries in agony. His face is not intimidating anymore.

It is as though his true nature is revealed. The three
century timid old man who killed his mother is frightened.
His face is wrinkled. He has lost his beastly appearance.
The *Whip of Righteousness*, which is a circus whip owned by
Reverend Bainbridge, glows sparkling with white fire. With
every strike the whip glows brighter and brighter as the
noonday sun. A choir of ANGELIC BEINGS sing a pitch and
sustain the words of DARLENE'S Hymn, *Lord of hope*.

> ANGELIC BEINGS
> You are. You are. My Matchless
> Lord of hope.

The ANGELIC BEINGS have four large wings as they sit in the
celestial clouds in the atmosphere of space above the earth.
They seem a lot closer to DARLENE as she watches the spectacle
while holding EARL in her lap sitting in the clouds. Her
hair blows in the winds above Buffalo's city line. Light
from the *Whip of Righteousness* sparkles a ray of light
connecting to every ANGELIC BEING in the celestial clouds.

The Bell Tower of Buffalo Methodist Cathedral of Mercy
reporter ANNA AGNES APPLEGATE broadcasts a live "Ammonothus
Sighting Special Report".

Captain Howard and reporter Applegate can hardly believe
what they are witnessing as they circle the Methodist
Cathedral of Mercy.

> AGNES ANNA APPLEGATE
> Captain Howard? Pull up higher.
> Buffalo New York we're watching live
> above the Methodist Cathedral of
> Mercy. Ammonothus the Wraith Man is
> being whipped by none other than the
> Reverend Thomas Henry Bainbridge and
> his wife, our beloved Sister Victoria
> Connie York-Bainbridge, who pastured
> this parish back in the early 1800's.

The wind carries the horrid cry of the AMMONOTHUS. Below
the citizens make their way toward the church. The police
vehicles follow behind.

> AGNES ANNA APPLEGATE (CONT'D)
> Hear the horrid cry of Ammonothus as
> the same circus whip the Reverend
> used when he was alive which causes
> the Wraith Master of Earl Harold
> Paul great pain.

The EHP Waste Management trucks surround the church as EARL'S
men wait for him to return to them from the sky.

AGNES ANNA APPLEGATE (CONT'D)
This is Reporter Agnes Anna Applegate
reporting live, hovering over Buffalo
Methodist Cathedral of Mercy near
Niagara Falls Park.

76 EXT. FBI HELICOPTER -- MOMENTS LATER   76

Agents ROGER, FELIX and NIGEL descend from the clouds in
their helicopter toward the Cathedral. The citizens of
Buffalo line the streets running towards the Cathedral of
Mercy. Some run in the streets. Others run away from the
Cathedral. Agent ROGER takes pictures. Agent Felix looks
through his binoculars at the crowd below.

FELIX puts down his binoculars and holds his digital high
end broadcast HD camera and films the areal view of the Bell
Tower of the Cathedral of Mercy as the FBI helicopter
approaches.

77 EXT. CELESTIAL CLOUDS ABOVE THE CATHEDRAL-(MINIATURE)   77 --
MOMENTS LATER

No one below or in the skies traveling by helicopter sees
DARLENE holding EARL who is laying in the lap of his childhood
friend. All eyes are watching the punishment of AMMONOTHUS.
The ANGELIC BEINGS begin to make a humming sound. Their
ears are made of wings standing erect three feet tall over
their heads. Their eyes are diamonds consumed in flames.
DARLENE looks in her lap at EARL HAROLD PAUL. She hears the
lash of the *Whip of Righteousness*.

                    DARLENE BAINBRIDGE
          Do you remember when we both received
          the Lash of Righteousness from our
          parents?

EARL still has his eyes closed. She cleans his face with
her hair and tears.

                    EARL HAROLD PAUL
          Darlene? I hear the lash of your
          father's whip. Is he going to hurt
          me? I remember when your father
          used to beat us. We were just kids.
          I was so afraid of the sound of a
          whip. I could never ever enjoy going
          to the circus. Until this day, I
          have my Butler take my children to
          the circus. I can't bear to hear
          that sound.

EARL covers his ears. DARLENE comforts him by caressing his
face.

EARL curls into a fetal position as he continues to lay on DARLENE'S lap. He looks into her eyes. He sees her hair blowing in the wind. Her face is illuminated.

She smiles at him. EARL smiles back, but the wind carries the sound of the *Whip of Righteousness*. EARL is troubled. He closes his eyes. He begins to vomit blood. His hands shake. He shivers all over. He closes his eyes tightly.

> DARLENE BAINBRIDGE
> Earl my dearest friend? Remember I
> told you I'd never leave you.

> EARL HAROLD PAUL
> Yes.

When he opens his eyes he sees DARLENE'S lovely face, however she is a little nine year old girl.

> DISSOLVE TO:

78 EXT. BUFFALO METHODIST CATHEDRAL OF MERCY COURTYARD --78 DAY

Buffalo New York, April 1864

The benediction has been given. Church members are leaving the Chapel into the courtyard. Some go straight off the church grounds while others linger in the immaculate garden courtyard. The church garden is a maze of flowers and plants.

The statues of the apostles, Matthew, Mark, Luke, Peter, and Paul with their names carved into the pedestal, they all stand on, are in the center of the garden. The six-foot sculptures are located separately in the courtyard. People are enjoying the courtyard walking and talking; children are playing on the lawn.

Near young EARL and DARLENE there are tree swings where kids like them are enjoying themselves. An open tomb of stone with a statue of Jesus of Nazareth standing in the doorway sits in the center of a manmade waterfall. Water flows from the mouth of Jesus. Some children chase ducks that swim toward the Jesus statue.

EARL is 10. DARLENE is 9. She is sitting against a tree. EARL is laying down with his head on her lap. Some adults are shocked and stare. They point fingers at EARL and DARLENE. Their innocent time together is misinterpreted.

EARL and DARLENE ignore the adults.

A quartet plays near the Jesus waterfall. The musicians perform a waltz.

The musical suite is a published hymn by young DARLENE BAINBRIDGE. A few church folk stand around the musicians as they play from sheet music *Lord of hope Hymn Suite*.

> YOUNG EARL
> Sing me that song you wrote, the
> waltz the musicians are playing now.
> I love hearing your hymns.

> YOUNG DARLENE
> Sure, if you sing with me ok, Earl?

> YOUNG EARL
> Ok Darlene.

> YOUNG EARL & DARLENE
> My Matchless Lord of hope. In me
> you'll forever reign. In your arms
> there's forgiveness left for me, in
> your arms if I only believe. How
> can I go on and deny, the power of
> your love so divine. In your arms
> there's forgiveness left for me, in
> your arms if I only believe. My
> Matchless Lord of hope. My Matchless
> Lord of hope. You are. You are.
> You are my Lord of hope.

DISSOLVE TO:

79 <u>EXT. CELESTIAL CLOUDS ABOVE THE CATHEDRAL-(MINIATURE)</u> -- NIGHT

We're back present day. The moonlight still illuminates the atmosphere over downtown Buffalo as the FBI helicopter and the Applegate News Chopper continue to circle the Bell Tower of the Methodist Cathedral of Mercy.

EARL is weeping and his tears defy gravity. DARLENE catches his tears and place them back down on his cheek. When she kisses his tears they stay and run down his face.

> EARL HAROLD PAUL
> I remember when we sang that song.
> I used to love to sing your hymns
> with you.

> DARLENE BAINBRIDGE
> I still write music. I am glad you
> remember it.

> EARL HAROLD PAUL
> Our parents were furious at us both.
> We were just kids. And they thought-

EARL weeps.

> DARLENE BAINBRIDGE
> I know. But you must forgive them.
> I have forgiven both our parents.

> EARL HAROLD PAUL
> I can't. I can't forgive them for
> what they did to us in the Cathedral
> Bell Tower.

> DARLENE BAINBRIDGE
> I forgive them but mostly I forgive
> you Earl, for the murders of my
> parents. My love abides for you
> still.

DISSOLVE TO:

80 **EXT. BUFFALO METHODIST CATHEDRAL BELL TOWER** -- **DAY**   80

Buffalo, New York April 1864

On the same Sunday morning after church the kids are taken
up the stairs to the Bell Tower. EARL and DARLENE'S parents
are closet *"swingers"*. The Reverend THOMAS HENRY BAINBRIDGE
and his wife Sister VICTORIA CONNIE YORK-BAINBRIDGE along
with EARL'S parents MARTHA MARGARET WILSON-PAUL and EARL SR.
are in the corner of the tower kissing. Suddenly, they swap
partners.

81 **INT. CATHEDRAL OF MERCY BELL TOWER** -- **CONTINUOUS**   81

In a corner, piles of rope used to ring the bell are neatly
stacked. Two roosters are fighting in the corner. Their
feathers cover the wooden floor, while in the opposite corner
EARL and DARLENE'S parents watch the roosters fight. They
look at their children strapped to the bell. Then EARL SR.
and THOMAS take turns kissing their wives.

People watching below cannot tell what is going on. They
only see young DARLENE and EARL tied by their wrists to the
side of the bell in the tower. They watch as the Reverend
takes turns with EARL SR. in whipping their kids with a circus
whip, known as the *"Whip of Righteousness"*.

EARL and DARLENE watch as their fathers kiss both of their
mothers in the corner of the tower.

> YOUNG EARL
> Father why are you kissing Sister
> Victoria?

                    REV.THOMAS HENRY BAINBRIDGE
          That's none of your business. What
          did you do to my daughter?

He whips EARL.

                    YOUNG DARLENE
          Father he did nothing to me. Please
          father believe me.

He whips DARLENE. Then the Reverend gives the whip to EARL
SR. and goes in the corner and puts his arm around his wife
VICTORIA and EARL'S mother MARTHA.

                    EARL HAROLD PAUL SR.
          You're lying. What did you do with
          my boy? Cut cut cut I'll cut your
          dirty rotten tongue. Don't you lie
          to me little girl.

He whips DARLENE.

                                        DISSOLVE TO:

82 EXT. CELESTIAL CLOUDS ABOVE THE CATHEDRAL-(MINIATURE)   82--
MOMENTS LATER

Present Day. The moon is directly over Downtown Buffalo.
The ANGELIC BEINGS are slowly disappearing from the horizon
outside earth's atmosphere of space and time. Searchlights
are pointed at he Bell Tower of the Cathedral of Mercy
Methodist Parish. The Spirits of EARL SR. and his wife
Margaret stand inside the tower. They look out over Buffalo
and notice their EARL laying down in the lap of DARLENE in
the clouds above them.

In the clouds EARL and DARLENE continue to hear the howling
cry of AMMONOTHUS as he is being whipped by the *"Whip of
Righteousness"* by the spirits of Reverend BAINBRIDGE and his
wife VICTORIA. Law enforcement and news helicopters fill
the midnight skies. The sound of the whip makes both EARL
and DARLENE jump in fear. EARL wipes his tears still being
caught by DARLENE, who kiss them in her hand then places
them back on his face. They immediately run down his face
and fall to the earth.

EARL tries to sing DARLENE'S *Lord of hope Hymn Suite*.

                    EARL HAROLD PAUL
          How can I go on and deny, the power
          of your love so divine-

As EARL'S tears flow, he is choked up with emotion and begins
to cry.

DARLENE continues singing the hymn where EARL left off.

> DARLENE BAINBRIDGE
> -In your arms there's forgiveness
> left for me, in your arms if I only
> believe.

EARL interrupts her sweet voice.

> EARL HAROLD PAUL
> I cannot. Darlene Bainbridge. I
> must destroy those men who prey on
> other men's wives. Those who cheat.

He tries to get up from her lap, but DARLENE holds him close
preventing him from leaving.

> DARLENE BAINBRIDGE
> You think you're doing God's service?

> EARL HAROLD PAUL
> I don't know. I kill because I must.
> I hate what Professor Jeremiah
> Peterson did to me, what he made me
> do to my wife Maple Mary. What both
> of your parents did to us.

> DARLENE BAINBRIDGE
> What our parents did to us was a
> long time ago.

The wind carries the cry of AMMONOTHUS who is still being
whipped in the Cathedral Bell Tower.

> EARL HAROLD PAUL
> I must free Ammonothus. He'll release
> him if I ask him too?

> DARLENE BAINBRIDGE
> My father, the great Reverend Thomas
> Henry Bainbridge that he is, would
> have no choice. Death and life are
> in the power of your tongue. You
> hold the key to your continued
> destruction.

> EARL HAROLD PAUL
> I hold the key. I must have him
> release Ammonothus at once.

DARLENE prevents EARL from leaving her lap. They smile while
gazing in each other's eyes.

                    DARLENE BAINBRIDGE
          Now I have you bound in my lap, Earl
          Harold Paul.

                    EARL HAROLD PAUL
          My life, what-

                    EARL & DARLENE
          What would it have been like if only
          I would have married you instead.

                    EARL HAROLD PAUL
          What became of your children?

                    DARLENE BAINBRIDGE
          Their descendants are on the earth
          still.

                    EARL HAROLD PAUL
          Don't tell me who they are.

                    DARLENE BAINBRIDGE
          Why not? You wouldn't hurt my
          children.

                    EARL HAROLD PAUL
          If they cheat on their wives. I'd
          cut their dirty rotten tongues out.

                    DARLENE BAINBRIDGE
          My son's descendants live just east...

                    EARL HAROLD PAUL
          Don't tell me. Don't show me.
          Promise me you'll never tell me.

DARLENE sheds some tears. EARL reaches out his hand. They
fall in his palm. When they touch the lines in his hand
they ascend defying gravity. EARL closes his eyes.

                    DARLENE BAINBRIDGE
          The stench of your wickedness not
          only causes your teats to defy gravity
          but even my tears can't stand the
          awful scent of your iniquities, Earl
          Harold Paul. Yet, in my heart my
          love for you still abides. I love
          you Earl Harold Paul with all the
          eternal love within me.

                    EARL HAROLD PAUL
          Your love, Your mercy is good for
          me, I know.
                         (MORE)

                    EARL HAROLD PAUL (CONT'D)
          Of my free will a wicked wretched
          wraith man I am...*Horrified*...by the
          absence of peace within the spirit
          of my mind. But I am, what I am.
          By choice. Darlene Bainbridge.

DARLENE holds back her tears. She can't. They fall on EARL'S
face defying gravity as she sings once more to him.

                    DARLENE BAINBRIDGE
          How can I go on and deny. The Power
          of your love so Divine. In your
          arms there's forgiveness left for
          me. In your arms if I only believe.

EARL opens his eyes and allows his tears to flow. His tears
are joined with hers as they ascend upwards. Into the air
over the Buffalo city line their tears are joined together
and are carried away with the wind. Their tears pass by the
Buffalo Cathedral Bell Tower.

THOMAS, VICTORIA, MARTHA and EARL SR. reach out and touch
their tears. EARL suddenly gets up and stands on the
celestial cloud.

DARLENE looks up into his eyes that are filled with hate.

A worm tunnel in the sky illuminates as more ANGELIC BEINGS
arrive over Buffalo in an array of colorful, dancing electric
light. The rolling celestial clouds are filled with energy
that causes an electrical storm.

As DARLENE vanishes, ANGELIC BEINGS sing her hymn. EARL
walks on the path of tears towards the Bell Tower. Suddenly,
DARLENE appears standing beside both of their parents.

                    EARL HAROLD PAUL
          Father. Mother. Reverend Bainbridge.
          Sister Bainbridge. Hold out your
          tongues. My childhood was cursed
          because of you. From me you'll taste
          eternal death. Your lust for one
          another has made you rotten. Rot
          rot rot...rotten!

He weeps as he stares at them and with one swing of his knife
he cuts their tongues. Immediately, they grow back. He
cuts their throats. They grow back instantly.

                    EARL SR,MARTHA,THOMAS&VICTORIA
          The Lord of hope forgave us. Have
          you forgotten? Didn't you know?
                    (MORE)

                    EARL SR,MARTHA,THOMAS&VICTORIA (CONT'D)
          We are forgiven and glorified. You
          are rotten.

                    DARLENE BAINBRIDGE
          I have forgiven my parents and you
          for murdering them. I've forgiven
          your parents. Earl you must too.

                    EARL HAROLD PAUL
          I can't. I won't. I love the power
          of unforgiveness. The immortality
          that the Ammonothus my Wraith Master
          offers me.

                    EARL SR,MARTHA,THOMAS&VICTORIA
          This is the life you have chosen of
          your own free will?

                    EARL HAROLD PAUL
          Yes. Of my own free will. I choose
          the path of destruction.

                    EARL SR,MARTHA,THOMAS&VICTORIA
          Of your own free will you choose to
          be unmerciful.

                    EARL HAROLD PAUL
          Yes. You are still holding
          Ammonothus!

                    EARL SR,MARTHA,THOMAS&VICTORIA
          Yes. Look around in this Bell Tower.

EARL stands on the Bell Tower brick twelve-foot windowless
pane. The FBI helicopter draws closer. Agent MADISON speaks
over the intercom.

                    ROGER MICKEY MADISON (V.O.)
          Earl Harold Paul come with us. Don't
          resist what you cannot escape. There
          is no where for you to run or hide.

EARL looks at the FBI helicopter. He sees the cop cars and
government Suburbans with their lights flashing. He sees
the Buffalo SWAT officers climb the brick wall of the
Cathedral Tower. Several officers shine a light in his face.

EARL looks into the crowd of citizens below. An APPLEGATE
NEWS helicopter hovers over closer. More officers enter the
church from on the ground. There is a sound at the door to
the Bell Tower. The SWAT Team pound their fists on the other
side of the door.

                    EARL HAROLD PAUL
         Where is Ammonothus? There he is
         release him. You're standing on
         him.

                    EARL SR,MARTHA,THOMAS&VICTORIA
         Well, where else would your Wraith
         Master be but underneath our feet!

                    EARL HAROLD PAUL
         Well...release him.

                    EARL SR.
         As you wish, my son. As you wish.

The door remains shut as police try to force entry. One at
a time they step down off of AMMONOTHUS THE WRAITH MAN.

                    DARLENE BAINBRIDGE
         Remember, Earl.

                    EARL HAROLD PAUL
         I know. You'll never leave me alone
         and I'll never change.

                    DARLENE BAINBRIDGE
         Then you'll never be cured from the
         sickness of self-destruction or from
         the destruction of others.

                    EARL HAROLD PAUL
         I don't wish or long to be cured.
         Good bye. My sweet friend.

EARL and DARLENE embrace. DARLENE looks in his eyes. Her
tears run down her face. His tears do not.

                    DARLENE BAINBRIDGE
         You will always be my dearest sweet
         friend.

DARLENE kisses EARL on his forehead. Their parents disappear.

                    DARLENE BAINBRIDGE (CONT'D)
         I am now your enemy. But I'll never
         hide my love from you. My love is
         more powerful than your hate.

EARL kisses DARLENE'S lips. He holds her illuminated body
tightly in his arms. The bells in the tower begin to chime
violently. Repeatedly. They sound louder than usual.

Buffalo Cathedral of Mercy begins to tremble. The ground
beneath the Parish begins to quake with tremors.

He opens his eyes seeing her beauty. When he closes them his tears escape his eyelids defying gravity.

DARLENE vanishes in his arms just as the police enter the Bell Tower. She soars into the worm hole tunnel in the sky. The ANGELIC BEINGS expand their wings that are as long as a football field. They escort her on a celestial cloud carried by turbulent winds. She begins to shine brighter than the moon. Her entire body continues to glow brighter and brighter. As she catches his tears and kisses them they fall to the earth like rain.

Suddenly, she becomes as the stars fixed in the heavens, as the worm hole disappears.

Her body breaks apart into shining particles of fire and light. Her every atom illuminates gloriously over Buffalo's city line.

EARL is amazed at DARLENE'S glory but then is distracted by FOOTSTEPS approaching him from behind. He hears many footsteps running up the Bell Tower stairwell. He turns toward the SWAT Team and FBI Agents.

83 <u>INT. BUFFALO METHODIST CATHEDRAL BELL TOWER</u> -- **CONTINUOUS**

Proudly, EARL HAROLD PAUL stands, with AMMONOTHUS towering behind him. AMMONOTHUS yells out his howling horrid cry. The whipping he received made his appearance to be like a timid old man. A man who is more than three centuries old.

His face becomes hideous and beastly in appearance. He has returned once again, transforming himself into an intimidating wicked wretched ghost creature, AMMONOTHUS THE WRAITH MAN. His voice sounds unearthly. His cry is not of this world, dimension, time or place. The frequency and pitch of his howling cry cause the SWAT officers and FBI Agents to cover their ears.

AMMONOTHUS vomits a liquid out of his mouth. The officers are covered in this substance. Suddenly, their hands burn like fire and become permanently fused into their skulls. Many other officers run down the stair well trying to escape the Bell Tower of the Parish. EARL takes a fifteen inch blade from inside the long robe of his Master. He makes his way through them, cutting their throats, ripping them open and taking their tongues out of their mouths.

The sound coming from AMMONOTHUS paralysis the law enforcement personnel in the tower. They can't think. They are disorientated. Like sheep they are prey and cannot escape the terror of AMMONOTHUS and EARL HAROLD PAUL.

84 <u>INT. STAIR WELL OF THE BELL TOWER</u> -- MOMENTS LATER   **84**

The stair well begins to sway back and forth continually as
EARL HAROLD PAUL and his Wraith Master make their way down
the steps. The howling of AMMONOTHUS causes the officers to
hide their face in the wall of the fire escape stair well.
Others urinate on themselves as they retreat to the bottom
of the tower, while other officers shake violently as if
becoming possessed, ramming their heads into the wall
repeatedly.

Suddenly, the entire police unit assigned in the stair well
turn around and run down the stairs screaming and trampling
over one another. Their mouths become deformed and remain
permanently wide open.

Standing on the bottom level are Agents ROGER, NIGEL, and
FELIX. They somehow remain unaffected as they look into the
eyes of EARL. The officers push the Agents out of their way
as they try to escape.

The lights inside the stair well go out. It is pitch black.
The Agents shine their flashlights into the eyes of EARL and
AMMONOTHUS as they make their way down the stairs.

The Agents look at the pictures of their wives in a pendant
they wear around their necks. They kiss the picture of their
wives.

>   ROGER MICKEY MADISON
>   Keep kissing the picture of your
>   wife in your silver lockets.
>   Concentrate on how much you love
>   her. We'll be fine.

>   NIGEL OSCAR KNOLL
>   Ok. What wickedness can over power
>   us when we know our wives love us?

>   NIGEL&FELIX&ROGER
>   Nothing!

>   FELIX FRANKLIN HAYES
>   The love we have for our wives casts
>   out all fear. This evil cannot and
>   will not harm us but we'll have to
>   apprehend Mr. Paul some other time.

The Cathedral stair well walls begin to crack.

>   FELIX FRANKLIN HAYES (CONT'D)
>   This Cathedral is strong but if we
>   stay we'll all be trampled upon.

> ROGER MICKEY MADISON
> Your right Agent Felix. Some other
> time. This Parish can stand this
> tremor caused by the Ammonothus
> wickedness however, this stair well
> won't hold much longer. To the
> helicopter!

> NIGEL OSCAR KNOLL
> What evil can harm us with the love
> of our wives in our hearts?

The Agents look up the swaying stairwell at EARL and
AMMONOTHUS.

> NIGEL&FELIX&ROGER
> Nothing! Some other time Ammonothus.
> Some other time Earl Harold Paul.

The Agents see EARL covered in blood from head to toe as he
hold a fist full of tongues and his knife. NIGEL, FELIX and
ROGER struggle their way out to the lawn of the Parish toward
their helicopter.

85 EXT. BELL TOWER -- MOMENTS LATER   **85**

The Agents run toward their helicopter. It begins to ascend
into the moonlight. EARL HAROLD PAUL stands at the door and
smiles as he lifts his hands that are filled with the tongues
of his victims. He walks through the crowd cutting their
throats and ripping out their tongues. The officers can't
get a clear shot. He hides himself in the crowd. AMMONOTHUS
spits FIRE BALLS out of his mouth, setting the police vehicles
on fire. The officers open fire on him. EARL walks to the
Cathedral of Mercy Road.

86 EXT. CATHEDRAL OF MERCY ROAD   **86**

EARL stands in the middle of the street outside the church
and sees lights approaching him. The headlights of the
vehicles are too bright to see the drivers that ram the
barricade of police vehicles. The EHP Waste trucks come to
a complete stop in front of Mr. Paul. Men in green EHP
uniforms get out of their trucks and march toward EARL.

EARL smiles. The street is filled with his tongueless prey
holding their throats suffocating to death.

> EARL HAROLD PAUL
> Men! Ladies! Take these Adulterers
> to the incinerator.

> EARL'S EMPLOYEES
> Yes. Earl Harold Paul.

EARL watches as his employees obey his orders.

Suddenly there is a sea of people coming from Niagara Falls
Park holding signs in protest against EARL and AMMONOTHUS.

AMMONOTHUS begins building human piles of weeping citizens
including law enforcement personnel. At super human speed,
one pile becomes four piles becomes twenty piles of people
stacked upon one another.

The crowd of citizens coming from the park try to retreat
but AMMONOTHUS catches them with lightning speed.

They are paralyzed under his power. They cannot move. They
are helpless as he continues to make human piles along
Cathedral of Mercy Road. Once more He opens his mouth and
fire shoots out of his mouth. The employees of EARL lift
the victims into the Waste trucks and begin driving away to
the EHP Plant.

87 **EXT. APPLEGATE NEWS HELICOPTER -- MOMENTS LATER**   87

Hovering above Cathedral of Mercy Road, Captain Howard follows
the path of humanity. Reporter APPLEGATE reports as before
her eyes watch in horror AMMONOTHUS at work. At incredible
speed more piles of humanity are being built.

88 **INT. APPLEGATE NEWS HELICOPTER -- CONTINUOUS**   88

There are tears in the eyes of AGNES as she reports the news.

                    AGNES ANNA APPLEGATE
               When Ammonothus the Wraith Man carries
               the citizens of Buffalo in his arms,
               they cannot move. They are paralyzed
               in his wicked power. What you're
               watching is a live broadcast from
               our Applegate News helicopter.

Captain HOWARD hovers the helicopter over the trash workers
as they pull the citizens from their piles casting them into
the EHP Waste trucks as AMMONOTHUS creates more piles.

                    CAPTAIN HOWARD
               Oh my God! I've never seen anything
               like this in my life.

The Applegate News Helicopter hovers over fifty piles of
humanity creating a maze the EHP Waste trucks maneuver
thorough.

                    AGNES ANNA APPLEGATE
               Stay away from Niagara Falls Park!
                    (MORE)

> AGNES ANNA APPLEGATE (CONT'D)
> Or risk becoming a human mountain of
> genocide, as piles of people are
> being stacked twelve-feet high.

89   **INT. FBI HELICOPTER** -- **MOMENTS LATER**   89

Agents NIGEL, FELIX and ROGER hover over Cathedral of Mercy
Road and over Niagara Falls Park nearby. ROGER holds an
Olympus Digital recorder as he speaks into the mic.

> ROGER MICKEY MADISON
> Every person Ammonothus touches turns
> into a stench of wickedness.

ROGER places the recorder back into his shirt pocket as NIGEL
navigates the helicopter higher in altitude. The Agents
witness a tornado of tears coming from the piles of humanity
ascending into the sky.

> FELIX FRANKLIN HAYES
> That's why all of the tears of the
> people are ascending into the sky.

Agent FELIX records AMMONOTHUS throwing hundreds of CITIZENS
into the back of the EHP Waste Trucks with his SONY HD camera.

> NIGEL OSCAR KNOLL
> The people's tears defy gravity to
> escape the powerful scent of
> Ammonothus.

> ROGER MICKEY MADISON
> It is the scent of death that causes
> their tears to defy gravity.

NIGEL notices the spirit of DARLENE BAINBRIDGE standing on
the top of the steeple of the Methodist Cathedral Bell Tower.

The Cathedral stops shaking. The tremors cease.

> NIGEL OSCAR KNOLL
> The tears of the people are forming
> into a tornado. Look how the wind
> is taking the river of tears to the
> top of the Methodist Cathedral of
> Mercy Bell Tower. Isn't that hymn
> composer Darlene Bainbridge?

> FELIX FRANKLIN HAYES
> Yes. Look-her parents and the parents
> of Earl Harold Paul are standing in
> the Tower.

90 <u>EXT. METHODIST CATHEDRAL OF MERCY STEEPLE</u> -- CONTINUOUS

The Spirit of DARLENE stands on the steeple. She watches
with tearful eyes the genocide of Buffalo and the maze of
humanity stacked twelve-feet high.

As the winds carry the people's tears to her, she stretches
out her hands. The winds carry the tornado of tears closer
toward her. The tornado wraps around her the Bell tower and
reaches into the clouds. The clouds begin to reflect
electrical energy. This energy forms a colorful display of
lightning as the thunder rolls across the sky.

She stretches out her hands and touches the tornado phenomenon
of tears. Suddenly she can see as far off into the EHP Waste
Management Plant as vehicles take the people to the
incinerator.

DARLENE sees through the walls of the Plant.

91 <u>EXT. EHP WASTE MANAGEMENT SYSTEMS PLANT WALL</u> --   91
CONTINUOUS

Using x-ray vision, she watches the employees at the plant
cast the citizens of Buffalo into the fire.

92 <u>EXT. EHP WASTE MANAGEMENT SYSTEMS PLANT FRONT GATE</u> -- 92
CONTINUOUS

Suddenly, DARLENE notices ANGELIC BEINGS filling the sky
over the Plant as EHP Waste garbage trucks bring loads of
people screaming to get out, beating their hands and feet
against the walls of the vehicle.

93 <u>EXT. NIAGARA FALLS PARK</u> -- CONTINUOUS   93

DARLENE notices the foggy moonlit sky above the falls that
are filled with a colorful display of light through the
celestial clouds as ANGELIC BEINGS appear filling the heavens.

94 <u>EXT. DOWNTOWN BUFFALO CITY LINE</u> -- CONTINUOUS   94

She also notices from the steeple of her father's Parish,
the skyline over downtown Buffalo and the rolling of colorful
celestial clouds as ANGELIC BEINGS reveal themselves in all
their glory.

95 <u>EXT. APPLEGATE NEWS HELICOPTER</u> -- MOMENTS LATER   95

Three Applegate News helicopters hover over the EHP Plant.
Agnes Anna Applegate watches above the glass dome roof as
the citizens of Buffalo are being cast into the incinerator.
She notices the ANGELIC BEINGS over the plant.

She watches as the angels descend though the roof and help the citizens out of the fires of the incinerators. The flames that once consumed them wither away. The people jump for joy in the arms of the ANGELIC BEINGS.

96 <u>**EXT. METHODIST CATHEDRAL OF MERCY STEEPLE**</u> -- CONTINUOUS

DARLENE allows her tears of compassion to fall to the earth. As her tears fall they become blazes of fireballs that travel to the EHP Plant.

97 <u>**EXT. EHP WASTE INCINERATORS**</u> -- CONTINUOUS   97

The fireballs sent by DARLENE enter the facility. The EHP employees are set on fire where they stand and melt away in the presence of the ANGELIC BEINGS who continue to rescue other victims from the flames of the incinerators.

98 <u>**EXT. NIAGARA FALLS PARK**</u> -- MOMENTS LATER   98

Standing upon twelve-foot high bodies of people who are still alive but are paralyzed under AMMONOTHUS THE WRAITH MAN'S power is EARL HAROLD PAUL who is holding a knife in one hand and a handful of bloody human tongues. He raises his hands over his head as he watches the skies above him and all around the Park fill with ANGELIC BEINGS. He sees DARLENE on a celestial cloud hovering over the Cathedral of Mercy.

99 <u>**EXT. METHODIST CATHEDRAL OF MERCY STEEPLE**</u> -- CONTINUOUS

When DARLENE sees EARL standing upon a pile of humanity, she touches the phenomenon tornado of tears still hovering all around her carried by the winds. The tears become fire balls out of her hand. The entire tornado of tears passes by the palm of her hands. They instantly become missiles of fire and travel in EARL'S direction. She watches as hundreds of EHP Waste Management workers in their dark green uniforms are set on fire which causes a chain reaction of fire from worker to worker all over the city.

100 <u>**EXT. NIAGARA FALLS PARK**</u> -- CONTINUOUS   100

EARL HAROLD PAUL places his hand on his head as he notices the fire balls of DARLENE set on fire all of his men and women throughout the park. AMMONOTHUS climbs on top of another pile of humanity as he notices through the maze of humanity mountains he constructed, the employees of EARL become consumed with fire and wither away.

EARL'S hands, at his own will, become fire. AMMONOTHUS turns his hands on fire. They stretch forth their hands at one another and release fire toward the other. They lower their hands setting ablaze the human piles they stand on.

EARL smiles with his evil grin. He watches as DARLENE soars
through the sky towards him. He motions her with fire blazing
hands to come to him. DARLENE BAINBRIDGE and EARL HAROLD
PAUL clench hands as they wrestle on top of the blazing
inferno of people.

**101 EXT. METHODIST CATHEDRAL OF MERCY BELL TOWER -- MOMENTS
LATER**

From the tower, DARLENE and EARL'S parents reach their hands
into the tornado of tears that still circles the Cathedral.
They cup their hands, taking a hand full of tears. With
their hands they guide the tornado towards the host of ANGELIC
BEINGS in the sky.

The ANGELIC BEINGS stretch forth their hands towards the
incoming tornado of fire blazing tears. Suddenly, the tornado
becomes rain falling to the earth and extinguishes the blazes
of humanity.

The piles of people all around the Cathedral become healed
of their paralysis. They stand on their feet and cheer.
The rain from the sky causes a chain reaction all over the
city.

102 EXT. NIAGARA FALLS PARK -- MOMENTS LATER   102

AMMONOTHUS THE WRAITH MAN finds himself consumed with the
ball of fire that ascended upon him from the Cathedral of
Mercy. He dives into the River Niagara and plunges into the
bottom of the Falls but the water does not consume the flames.
The ANGELIC BEINGS stretch forth their hands over the Park
and rain from the heavens extinguishes the blazing piles of
humanity.

EARL and DARLENE find themselves falling to the ground as
the people they were standing on are able to free themselves.

The citizens in the Park make a circle around DARLENE and
EARL as they struggle to subdue the other. EARL finds it
difficult to withstand DARLENE'S strength. DARLENE puts
EARL into a choke hold. He struggles to free himself but he
can't and quits. As he looks in her loving eyes, EARL HAROLD
PAUL stops fighting and finds himself with his head in the
lap of DARLENE BAINBRIDGE. She kisses him on his cheek.

                    DARLENE BAINBRIDGE
          I told you Earl Harold Paul I would
          never leave you alone. Your acts of
          violence have made you my enemy but
          I forgive you for killing my parents
          and yours. I forgive you for the
          genocide you've committed against
          the citizens of Buffalo.

DARLENE has tears in eyes.

>   DARLENE BAINBRIDGE (CONT'D)
>   I love you Earl. I always will.

EARL begins to lose consciousness as a tear falls out of his
eye and beings to ascend. DARLENE grabs the tear. She kisses
her hand and allows the tear to roll off her hand on to his
cheek. The tear rolls down his face to the ground.

EARL HAROLD PAUL opens his eyes wide as he looks at her. He
then shuts them and falls into unconsciousness.

She holds him in her arms tightly.

Reporter AGNES ANNA APPLEGATE and Captain HOWARD hover over
the park toward the water fall in their helicopter.

The FBI helicopter lands in the Park near DARLENE and EARL.
Agents ROGER, NIGEL and FELIX leave the helicopter and walk
toward DARLENE and EARL through the crowd.

The crowd looks up and notices that the ANGELIC BEINGS are
singing the Hymn Suite *Lord of hope*. They all join the
ANGELIC BEINGS as they stand in the park.

>   ANGELIC BEINGS & CITIZENS (V.O.)
>   How can I go on and deny the power
>   of your love so divine. In your
>   arms there's forgiveness left for
>   me.

DARLENE begins to sing with the crowd and ANGELIC BEINGS in
the clouds.

>   DARLENE BAINBRIDGE
>   In your arms if I only believe. You
>   are. You are. My Matchless Lord of
>   hope. You are. You are. My
>   Matchless Lord of hope.

The FBI Agents stand within five feet of the Spirit of
DARLENE. The Buffalo SWAT Team moves through the crowd while
pushing them back behind them. The SWAT Team surrounds the
Agents, DARLENE and EARL.

Their weapons are drawn.

>   ROGER MICKEY MADISON
>   Are you the Spirit of Darlene
>   Bainbridge?

> DARLENE BAINBRIDGE
> Yes. And this is my childhood friend
> Earl Harold Paul.

When the agents kneel down to take EARL, DARLENE holds him tighter, kissing his cheek.

> DARLENE BAINBRIDGE (CONT'D)
> You've come to take him from me.

> ROGER MICKEY MADISON
> He must come with us.

As ROGER, FELIX and NIGEL take EARL out of the arms of the Spirit of DARLENE, a *Boeing Chinook* airlifts AMMONOTHUS THE WRAITH MAN who is still consumed in flames.

As the flames wither away he is flown above the trees to a nearby Peter-Built flat-bed tractor and trailer. Standing near their vehicle JETHRO and WESLEY give hand signals to the pilot who lowers AMMONOTHUS on to the flat-bed trailer.

FBI Agents in dark glasses and jumpsuits along with the New York National Guard place chains on him, securing AMMONOTHUS THE WRAITH MAN to the bed of the trailer.

EARL HAROLD PAUL is carried to a Chevy Suburban. The Peter-Built and the caravan of black Suburbans drive through the Park to cheering crowds of citizens. The caravan heads downtown.

DARLENE BAINBRIDGE soars upward into the clear moonlit sky above Niagara Falls. Her body explodes into fires of light that become shooting stars. Her figure becomes imprinted into the heavens over the city skyline and Niagara Falls Park.

The ANGELIC BEINGS disappear into another dimension of time and space in a worm hole of celestial clouds that becomes a blinding light of colors filling the sky like a fireworks display until the moonlit night is completely clear.

There is not a cloud in the sky as the moon rests twelve o'clock high over Buffalo.

                                             DISSOLVE TO:

103 **EXT. FBI HEADQUARTERS BUILDING -- MOMENTS LATER**   **103**

The crowd cheers as the FBI and Police vehicles pass by.

The procession heads into the FBI Headquarters. Agents ROGER, NIGEL and FELIX get out of the Suburbans and walk beside the

vehicle as the crowd walks along side of them singing the
Hymn Suite *Lord of hope.*

Agent ROGER MICKEY MADISON looks up and notices the Spirit
of DARLENE BAINBRIDGE standing on the very top of the FBI
Building. Her parents and EARL'S parents are standing on
the outside edge of the lofts.

Standing proudly and looking over downtown Buffalo DARLENE
BAINBRIDGE begins to smile as her long hair flows in the
wind in the full moon light. She brightens the entire city
with her glory and beauty.

                                        FADE TO BLACK:

FADE IN: *TEXT APPEARS*

SEVEN MONTHS LATER

                                        DISSOLVE TO:

104 <u>INT. APPLEGATE TELEVISION NEWS ROOM</u> -- MORNING   104

Interns hustle around the news room floor carrying paper
work to the AGNES'S desk. Three camera operators focus their
lenses. A crane camera hovers over the News Room floor.
Media-mogul and News Anchor AGNES ANNA APPLEGATE is seated
at her desk watching behind her a wall of sixty-inch plasma
screens. She reviews the typed notes given to her by interns
while makeup artists complete her hair and makeup.

An African-American Director blows his whistle.

The newsroom crew laughs him to scorn. AGNES is watching
the screen never taking her eyes off of EARL as he is being
led away in chains surrounded by the SWAT Team, US Marshals
and Police officers ANITA CRUZ and Lt. JACQUELINE JENKINS
out of the Courtroom.

The director's frowns makes the crew laugh at him more as he
blows his whistle again holding up his hand.

The newsroom crew quiets their chatter.

                    TV DIRECTOR
          Let's have some quiet! In five.
          Four. Three. Two.

APPLEGATE swivels her chair around toward the cameras.

                    AGNES ANNA APPLEGATE
          Good day Buffalo.
                    (MORE)

                    AGNES ANNA APPLEGATE (CONT'D)
          As you can see Buffalo's Finest are
          escorting Earl Harold Paul out of
          the Federal Court house.

EARL looks into the camera and smiles. The studio monitors
televise with audio and live picture.

                    EARL HAROLD PAUL
          Adulterers stay away from Buffalo,
          New York.

                    AGNES ANNA APPLEGATE
          Who is this man to become a judge
          over the citizens of this city? He
          is the *finger of God*...so he believes.
          It is said that even the stench of
          his own wickedness causes his tears
          to defy gravity.

The live picture feed of EARL'S face freezes.

                    AGNES ANNA APPLEGATE (CONT'D)
          There is no room for mercy in the
          heart of Earl Harold Paul. Sources
          tell Applegate News that Ammonothus
          the Wraith Man will be transported
          by Government caravan to an
          underground FBI Prison in AREA 51.

A prerecorded video shot in HD broadcast the *Boeing Chinook*
lowering AMMONOTHUS to the flat-bed Peter-Built in chains.

                    AGNES ANNA APPLEGATE (CONT'D)
          Of course I can't confirm the
          existence of an underground government
          prison at AREA 51, but one thing is
          certain. There is no need to fear
          him any longer. For Applegate News
          in downtown Buffalo, this is Agnes
          Anna Applegate reporting. Have a
          wonderful summer day!

                                        FADE OUT:

FADE IN:

105 <u>EXT. NIAGARA FALLS PARK</u> -- DAY   105

A group of prisoners are cleaning up the Park. Tourists are
taking pictures of the prisoners as they clean the park near
the edge of the cliffs of the falls. The prisoners are
secured to each by one long chain.

EARL HAROLD PAUL is surrounded by guards bound in ankle chains. He picks up trash off the grass and rock bed cliff and stuffs it in a trash bag. The two Italian males in their 30's are pushing him closer to the edge of the cliff.

> PRISON GUARD 1
> Hey Earl I cheat. I love it.

> PRISON GUARD 2
> Don't get too close. He'll rip out
> your tongue.

A group of prisoners run to the aid of EARL. They fall over themselves as they come near to him. The other guards surround them.

106 INT. CARLA'S R/T CHARGER -- MOMENTS LATER   106

Carla drives her polished R/T through the Park closer to the three federal prison buses. EMMA is seven months pregnant and is massaging her stomach.

> CARLA VIVIAN VAN HOLT-WILLIAMS
> Tell your husband I said thank you
> for killing my husband.

> EMMA PETERSON
> I will Agent Van Holt.

The R/T parks in front of the prison buses.

107 EXT. NIAGARA FALLS PARK -- CONTINUOUS   107

Agents ROGER, FELIX and NIGEL greet EMMA who ignores them. CARLA and her fellow agents hurry along to keep up with EMMA as they escort her to meet her husband.

EMMA leave them running into the arms of EARL through the procession of prisoners near the bed cliff. He places his cuffed hands over EMMA. They embrace. They look over the river Niagara.

> EMMA PETERSON
> Niagara Falls. I love this place.
> I would not want us to live anywhere
> else.

> EARL HAROLD PAUL
> I don't know how long I'll allow
> them to keep me here. But I know
> I'll stay their prisoner for at least
> two more months. Until our twin
> sons are born.

                    EMMA HAROLD PAUL
          Thank you.

She kisses EARL passionately.

                    EMMA HAROLD PAUL (CONT'D)
          You know why I married you?

                    EARL HAROLD PAUL
          So after seven months you're finally
          going to tell me?

In EMMA'S eyes there are tears. They escape her eyes and
ascend into the sky.

                    ROGER MICKEY MADISON
          Ok that's enough. We're taking you
          to the governments new federal prison.

                    EMMA HAROLD PAUL
          What? Where?

                    NIGEL OSCAR KNOLL
          Area 51 Mrs. Paul.

                    FELIX FRANKLIN HAYES
          Area 51 has a new prison for you and
          Ammonothus the Wraith Man along with
          others of your kind.

                    EMMA HAROLD PAUL
          I told you what I'd do if you took
          me from my wife before our sons were
          born.

                    CARLA VIVIAN VAN HOLT-WILLIAMS
          Your wife is coming too.

                    EMMA HAROLD PAUL
          Am I a prisoner?

                    EARL HAROLD PAUL
          Our sons. You want my boys! I'll...

                    CARLA VIVIAN VAN HOLT-WILLIAMS
          No you won't I'll kill your sons
          right now.

                    EMMA HAROLD PAUL
          Is it loaded?

CARLA fires her weapon in the air. The weapon does not
misfire this time. CARLA points her pistol at EMMA'S stomach.

                    EMMA HAROLD PAUL (CONT'D)
          Ok. But you'll have to travel the
          interstate. I want to spend as much
          time as possible near my wife. You'll
          separate us both for God knows how
          long.

                    ROGER MICKEY MADISON
          God? You speak the name of God?

The FBI Agents laugh.

                    NIGEL OSCAR KNOLL
          For that, you just earned yourself a
          road trip.

ROGER, FELIX, NIGEL and CARLA escort EMMA and EARL HAROLD
PAUL into the same black Chevy Suburban.

                                        DISSOLVE TO:

108 **EXT. NM INTERSTATE 40 WEST** -- **NIGHT**   108

Welcome to New Mexico. The six black Suburban FBI caravan
travels at high speeds. The Suburbans are followed by four
Peter-Builts and trailers and one flat-bed driven by JETHRO
and WESLEY. Another flat-bed carries CARLA'S R/T.

                                        DISSOLVE TO:

109 **EXT. NV STATE HWY 95 SOUTH** -- **MORNING**   109

It is just before Sunrise and there is not a cloud in the
sky. The FBI caravan is joined by twelve Nevada Highway
Patrol cars as they pass by the road sign that reads: Las
Vegas 25 miles.

110 **EXT. CHEVY SUBURBAN** -- **CONTINUOUS**   110

Seated next to one another, EMMA takes EARL'S hand and places
it on her stomach. EARL presses the window button. EMMA'S
hair flows in the wind.

                    EARL HAROLD PAUL
          You still have not told me Emma.

She looks at him with tears in her eyes. They defy gravity
resting at the top of the Suburban. The tears fill the
passenger window as they are shut by NIGEL. The Agents do
not yet discover the phenomenon.

111 <u>EXT. AREA 51 GOVERNMENT BUNKER 5</u> -- MOMENTS LATER   111

A gate opens at AREA 51. The guard at the gate waves the
caravan on to the property. The Suburbans and the Peter-
Builts drive to bunker 5 where armed Marines line up. Men
and women in white suits and dark glasses run toward the
caravan.

>   ROGER MICKEY MADISON
>   Let's go. Earl you've had your road
>   trip.

>   EARL HAROLD PAUL
>   Wait a minute.

>   ROGER MICKEY MADISON
>   Get out. Now!

Agent ROGER and the other agents notice the drops of rain
escaping into the atmosphere from inside the Suburban.

>   EMMA HAROLD PAUL
>   Our marriage and my devotion to you
>   has made me a powerful wicked and
>   wretched woman. After all, you know
>   all too well what my greatest
>   obsession is about you, Earl Harold
>   Paul.

>   EARL HAROLD PAUL
>   Emma Harold Paul? You love the smell,
>   the scent of death?

>   EMMA HAROLD PAUL
>   I love the way the scent of death
>   smells on you.

As they kiss passionately, their thirst is quenched.

                                        FADE TO BLACK:

                                        DISSOLVE TO:

                         <u>**THE END.**</u>

*NOTE: As **Credits roll** over the words "THE END" that fills
the screen it disappears into infinity, Raymond Harrison's
Main Title Score begins performed by the Mount Harrison
Pictures Studio Orchestra. The audience is listening to
vocalist sing the Wicked Wretched Wraith Men Suite.*

Mount Harrison Pic-tures Stu-di-os   Mount

Harri-son   Pictures Studi - os

En-joy your next   mo-tion   Pic - ture show.

From Raymond Harrison En-

-joy your new birthplace of i- magina- tion mount

Harri-son Pic-tures studi-os

Lord of Hope Hymn Suite

Music & Lyrics by Raymond Harrison

Lord of hope my matchless Lord of hope. You
Are my Lord of hope In
you I'll for e — ver reign. In your

MOUNT HARRISON PICTURES STUDIOS PRESS

Lord of Hope Hymn Suite   Music & Lyrics by
Raymond Harrison

MOUNTHARRISONPICTURESSTUDIOSPRESS

CHORUS

"Mount Harrison Pictures Studios!"
"Mount Harrison Pictures Studios!"
[music interlude]
"Mount Harrison Pictures Studios!"

1st Verse

"Enjoy your next Motion Picture Show, from
Raymond Harrison.
Enjoy your new birthplace of imagination...
Mount Harrison Pictures Studios!"

CHORUS

The Story Worlds,
The Story Worlds
The Story Worlds of Fiction!
Enjoy Raymond Harrison...
Repeat 2x

1st Verse

I love to release the story worlds of fiction,
from my mind.
From my mind,
from my mind, from my mind.
The Story Worlds of Fic-tion!

"Lord of hope Hymn Suite"
Lyrics by Raymond Harrison

CHORUS

Lord of hope,
My Matchless Lord of hope!

1ˢᵗ Verse

My Matchless Lord of hope.
In you I'll forever reign.
In you arms there's forgiveness left for me.
In your arms if I'll only believe.
How can I go on and deny,
the power of your love so divine.
In your arms there's forgiveness left for me.
In your arms if I'll only believe.
"You are.
You are.
My Matchless Lord of hope."
* repeat *
Lord of hope.

"Death Song Suite"
Lyrics by Raymond Harrison

CHORUS

Adulterer you'll die die die!
Your dirty rotten tongue is filled with lies.
Cut cut cut, I'll cut your tongue, so you won't taste,
taste taste taste, the sweet ravishing flavor of another
man's wife!

Author's Note: While the lyric of the "Death Song Suite" is violent in nature, it portrays a fictional character who enlists the help of others to commit acts of violence upon others; Mr. Raymond Harrison does not believe that people or himself should act in the manner portrayed in the fictional character Earl Harold Paul and his followers. This work is about Good vs. Evil, about a man who gave his life to the power of Unforgiveness and about a Hymn Composer who tried to warn him of the consequences of his actions. This work is a FANTASY/THRILLER an original work of fiction for entertainment. Mr. Harrison, his film production company and publishing company Mount Harrison Pictures Studios and Mount Harrison Pictures Studios Press does not and will not enlist, condone or encourage violence.
Mr. Harrison believes that all injustice inflicted upon himself and/or others should be handled by his/and your local Government Court and Justice System.

"Wicked Wretched Wraith Men"
Lyrics by Raymond Harrison

CHORUS

Wicked! Wicked! Wretched, Wraith Men!
Wicked! Wicked! Wretched Wraith Men!
* repeat *
Wicked Wretched Wraith Men!
Wicked Wretched Wraith Men!
Wicked! Wicked! Wretched Wraith Men!

1st Verse

Without my Lord's Grace, I'd be lost at sea...
I'd sink, I'd sink, I'd sink "in the waves"
of my iniqui---ties!
I'd drown..."Oh yes I'd drown", I could not stay alive,
"Why?"
All because of my wicked life.
My "wick-wick, wicked life!"

2nd Verse

I gave my life to the "Wicked Wraith of Night"
My friend the Hymn Composer told me, "Put away,
put away my knife!"
I desired---to take, the Adulterer's wanton life,
After all, he stole my Maple Mary! "Maple Mary, my
sweet wife!"

3rd Verse

Without my Lord's Grace, I'd be wretched just like
he, my parents were murdered, when I was young, I
escaped from the Prison of Hate!
"Gate of Prison Hate!"
Wicked-----wicked Unforgiveness, Search! Hey!
You'll never find me!
I'm hiding behind my Lord's face!
I'm invisible don't you see?

4th Verse

I gave my life to the "Wicked Wraith of Night!"
Adulterers beware, I always keep my knife with me.
I'm not fill--ed with love, like the Hymn Composer
a---bove! I dream of Peace Unforgiveness has my
soul, my soul, my soul. I dream of Peace
Unforgiveness has my soul, my soul, my soul!

BRIDGE

Wraith Men...Wicked Wretched, Wicked Wretched
Wraith Men!
Wraith Men... Wicked Wretched, Wicked Wretched
Wraith Men!
Wraith Men...Wicked Wretched, Wicked Wretched
Wraith Men!
The horrid and tragic tales of Earl Paul,
"Mr. Earl Harold Paul!"

Raymond Harrison was born at the Philadelphia Naval Base Hospital.
He is a Persian Gulf U.S. Army Veteran. He lives in Southern California and is presently
working on the prequels and sequels to this creative work.

There will be nine "Wicked Wretched Wraith Men" stories published by
Mr. Harrison.
For more horrid and tragic tales of Earl Harold Paul,
Mount Harrison Pictures Studios Press Fans
"Stay tooned"...